The Adjustable Diet Cookbook

THE
Adjustable Diet
COOKBOOK

by Suzy Chapin

Funk & Wagnalls: New York

Published by Funk & Wagnalls, *A Division of*
Reader's Digest Books, Inc.

Printed in the United States of America

THIS BOOK IS FOR MAMA
THE LITTLE OLD LADY

Robert E. Windom, M.D. Internal Medicine William L. Page, M.D.
Cardiology

1750 South Osprey Avenue
Sarasota, Florida 33579

Mrs. R. K. Chapin   *April 1, 1966*
Colonia, New Jersey

Dear Susie:

I am very pleased to report to you that your mother has lost
another pound since her last visit of two weeks ago.

When I first saw her, she weighed 157 pounds and since she has
been coming to me has reached a high of 161 pounds. Her weight
today is 126½ pounds.

I understand there has been some criticism of your diet, the
theory being that no one can eat this few calories and remain
healthy.

I would like to report that your mother has never looked better
and she looks at least ten years younger. Her figure is greatly
improved and she undoubtedly feels much, much better with the
decreasing problems with her back. She certainly is far from
becoming unhealthy on the diet.

Let me wish you lots of encouragement and luck with your book
and I must say that I certainly admire you.

Sincerely,

(Bill)

William L. Page, M.D.

Contents

The Adjustable Diet and You

It takes months, usually years, to assemble enough excess weight to be classified as a weight problem. It cannot be done overnight: you didn't get fat yesterday. How did you find out you were fat—fat enough to be worried about it? Was it the doctor during your annual checkup who said "This extra weight must go"? Perhaps not. Maybe you were standing in a fitting room vainly trying to zip yourself into your usual size. Did you catch an unexpected glimpse of yourself in a mirror and wonder "Who is that fat woman in a dress like mine?" Was it your best friend who brought it to your attention? Or an unflattering candid photograph? Maybe you overheard a chance remark.

However it was, here you are, fat, unhappy, uncomfortable, unhealthy. You have tried to diet. Every new fad diet that came down the pike you hopped on for a couple of weeks. Sure, you lost weight, but you gained it all back, and usually a few pounds extra. By that time there was a new crazy diet to try. In despair you turned to your doctor (or, if you haven't, you should have). He handed you a little booklet or a diet list, told you to stay on a certain number of calories a day, gave assorted advice for your particular needs, maybe even some pills, and told you to come back in one or two weeks. The first week, in the first bloom of enthusiasm, you lost two or three pounds. The loss slowed up the second week. The third—oh, woe is you—you gained!

Having spent all this time slowly gaining weight, you must

realize that it is going to take you just as long to remove it. Most quickie diets have serious flaws, and if you do manage to stay on one for several months you will undoubtedly find yourself back at the doctor's office with added ills for your trouble. A proper diet, aside from being low in calories, must be *nutritionally sound*. It must also be *attractive* enough to keep you from being bored with it!

One of the great drawbacks to dieting successfully is the fact that most people do not live alone. If you are a wife and mother you are cooking for all those thin people—children who can eat you out of house and home, husbands who won't eat diet food even when they need it, your bridge club, your elderly aunt, or just anyone. Maybe you are not the one who must diet, but the doctor has put your husband on a diet and frightened you into seeing that he stays on it. DO NOT DESPAIR. *The Adjustable Diet* was made to answer these problems, and if you will follow the rules you will have a new way of life.

It is possible to live, lose weight, and enjoy life on as little as 600 calories a day. Many people can lose weight eating 1200 calories a day or even 1800. Your doctor can guide you at this point. The basic menu for each day as set forth here is for 600 calories a day for reasons set forth below. Every day there is a new and different menu, carefully worked out so that it is superior in filling your nutritional needs. I am aiming my advice at women because (let's face it) we are still the ones who control what comes into the house to be cooked, eaten, and digested. Feed the nondieting people the same basic dinner; just enlarge their portions. There are added benefits: Teenage complexions mysteriously start to clear, waistlines slowly diminish, collars become looser. Be sure that each of your young ones has a quart of milk a day. Follow the dessert recipes carefully and they will never know. Cook rice, potatoes, or pasta for the nondieters; sometimes (if it says so on the diet), the dieter may even have a little bit—you know, what's curry without rice? Lunch in this country is a movable feast, so you can diet at home having sent off the lunchbox set with their peanut-butter and jelly sandwiches. The basic diet you are giving them will make up for any deficiencies they have.

Why and How This Book Was Written

About a year ago I had to go on a rescue mission to Florida. My little old lady, my FAT little old lady, was being held in the hospital until I could get there to free her. The doctors would not let her go home alone, and she was in about as poor shape as she could get and still be breathing. The upshot of the whole thing was that she had to go on a diet and lose weight—a lot of weight—so much that her two doctors, the heart man and the bone man, would not say how much or how long they thought it would take to do it.

The only definite thing was the amount of calories a day: 600. This was a shocker. Mother and I have always been "food nuts"; we love to cook and eat, and for at least twenty-five years we have both been on and off all sorts of diets; name one, we've tried them *all*. Six hundred calories was the greatest challenge we have ever had, but I am happy to tell you that my little old lady (and now she really *is* little) and I have slain this dragon. Little old ladies who lead sedentary lives—sitting, watching television, playing cards, knitting, doing needlepoint, riding in cars and elevators instead of walking—cannot lose weight while consuming 1200 calories a day. The little old ladies must get back on their fat little feet and do some walking every day if possible. Walk after every meal, before bedtime, whenever possible. At first, my little old lady would totter around the apartment leaning on the furniture. She is doing much better now. She can't walk upstairs because of the dicky heart, but she walks down.

I am not saying that any of this was easy; it took courage and determination, but it has been worth the effort. It is worth it when her back doesn't hurt, when she doesn't have indigestion, when all her supposedly chronic intestinal disorders have disappeared, when she wears her size-10 shift, and especially when her doctor smiles at her and says he doesn't know how she did it. Well, this is how. Shape up. Get a grip. Keep your sense of humor and STICK WITH THIS DIET.

This diet plan has worked so well for my little old lady that we want to share it with other fat little old ladies, fat middle-aged ladies, overweight gentlemen whatever their ages, unhappy lumpy teenagers, young mothers who can't seem to lose after that second (or even first) baby. The basic plan is for 600 calories a day, but *do not diet without consulting your doctor.* If you and he decide you can lose on 1200 calories a day simply double the amounts of foods as given. If you can lose on 1800 calories (most men can), multiply by 3. If you are cooking for your nondieting husband, just follow the recipes as given and let him eat all he wants, while you measure and weigh your 600 calories. The food is delicious and he won't suspect it is diet food. It is low-fat and low-sugar and low-calorie, all carefully disguised as wonderful food.

The worst thing about dieting is the complete and utter boredom that sets in after a week or two of broiled meat, fish, and chicken. This is why many diets fail. The dieter goes off the diet, *has* to have dessert, can't make it without some exotic dish such as Boeuf Stroganoff, chile con carne, chocolate mousse, or lasagna. If you have forty or fifty pounds to lose it is just too dull and too hard.

This book is divided into four sections, six weeks of daily menus for each season of the year. If you stick on this diet for six months you will not only have lost weight; you will have changed your way of cooking and eating. You will feel better, you will look younger, and you will really enjoy living.

You don't have to be rich to go on this diet because you will save so much money by not buying heavy cream, ice cream, cakes, pies, butter, bakery goods, and candy that you will not notice the bite when you buy lobster or raspberries. You will also save money on doctor bills, digestive aids, and other unpleasant things.

The recipes give varied numbers of servings, from 1 to 8 or 10, for an angel cake. Just because you are on a diet doesn't mean that you can't entertain your friends, feed your family, and behave very much as you always have. However, there is one important thing: on 600 calories a day you cannot drink. Booze, that is. There isn't enough leeway; you would die of malnutrition. An ounce of almost any kind of liquor is approximately 100 calories. So until you have lost enough weight to increase your intake of calories you will have to go "off the sauce." But you can show up at the cocktail hour if you bring your own bottle of low-calorie (1 calorie per 6-ounce glass) ginger ale, cola, root beer, or any other flavor, found easily at your friendly neighborhood supermarket; or when you entertain at home serve yourself and no one will be the wiser. If you want to save up 25 calories early in the day "blow the bit" with 4 ounces of tomato juice, or have a Naked Bull Shot (beef bouillon without the vodka). My little old lady said it wasn't worth the sacrifice of saving up all day just to spend 100 calories on a drink before dinner.

Easing Into the Diet

The first week or two of the diet it is usually easier to stay home and not get too involved with other people. You will probably be feeling a little light-headed and not quite yourself while your stomach adjusts to the smaller amounts of food you will be eating. This is normal; it will go away after a couple of weeks. Also, in a couple of weeks, when you will have lost some weight, you will be fired with determination to continue and your will power, your most important dieting ally, will be strengthened. But don't cut yourself off from the world. If there is another person who is interested in your diet and your progress it will help you to talk to him or her. It helped my little old lady to have me around urging her on to better things. If you should be wavering, a little admiring conversation can put some starch in your spine. You will come to see that your meals at home are so exotic, interesting, appealing, and delicious that dining out will hold no thrill. Remember that when you go out to dinner you also run the risk of encountering those helpful souls who, knowing full well that you are on a diet, will serve Double Dutch Chocolate cake and say "Oh, just a *little* slice won't hurt you." Not much! It takes real guts to remain polite and with a brave smile say "No thank you." It takes time for anyone to develop this exemplary behavior, so don't risk it too early in the game.

Now for a serious chat about nutrition. It may seem ridiculous to discuss nutrition when you are on the 600-calorie-a-day regime, but every one of those 600 calories must pay off nutritionally. You will be in serious trouble if you *don't* pay attention. You are in some sort of trouble already or you wouldn't be reading this book.

You are too fat, and because you are too fat, there probably are lots of things you have given up discussing with your doctor. Most doctors don't get all steamed up about nutrition and vitamins. Even the United States Public Health Service has come out saying that the average American does not need extra vitamins. Maybe so, but when you are dieting, whether you are on 600 or 1200 or 1800 calories a day, you *must* take a multiple-vitamin tablet that contains minerals every day. Ask your doctor; he'll probably say "Yes, if you want to." Also, check with your doctor about using an artificial sweetener. If he says all right, go ahead; but also setp up your intake of Vitamin C. That is why whenever I say lemon, even in tea, don't skip it. (Lemon contains Vitamin C.) The food you eat must be high in nutritional quality. There are foods and drinks that contain empty calories: the prime example, to me, is a chocolate ice cream soda. Lots of calories that don't do a thing for you except make you fat. This is what you must avoid. Every mouthful you take during this diet should be the highest-quality food you can find—the freshest fruit, eggs, vegetables, the best meat, the skimmest milk.

Skim milk has exactly the same nutritional value whole milk has, except that the fat has been removed. If you can't stand skim milk (incidentally, you *must* get rid of some of these foolish notions), there are certain brands of fresh milk on the market today that have had most of the fat removed, vitamins added, and in addition are homogenized. They taste and look like the real article. Golden Gurn-Z is our favorite, but you may find one you like more. Experiment. Dried skim milk is a great saver, both of money and calories. Milk is vitally important to you. It is good for your bones, and if you drink some every day you will probably be spared osteoporosis, a softening of the bones in most older people resulting from depletion of calcium. Sitting is bad for your bones, because this also causes the calcium to diminish. Did you know that they carefully check the calcium content of the astronaut's bones after each flight because weightlessness can be bad, too? If there is not enough calcium in your bones they become brittle and break, and there you are in traction, all unhappy. Calcium is good for your arthritis, too; almost everybody is likely to become somewhat arthritic sooner or later, and milk helps ward it off.

If some of the things on this diet seem odd to you, be adventurous. Try them. My little old lady loves to eat, and she was afraid that going on a diet would take all the fun and adventure out of her gastronomic life. She found that there were wonderful things in store for her, and so will you, when you try it. You must take an interest; you must take the trouble to follow the recipes exactly as given; don't fall back into the old ways of eating because they are familiar to you. They are usually the fattening ways, the ways *you* got *fat*.

Devote *all* your time and *all* your energy to the diet in the beginning. Concentrate on it. It isn't easy; there is nothing magical about it, but YOU WILL SUCCEED. The longer you try, the easier, it will be, and you will find that you have changed your life.

Advice, Instructions, Cautions, and Comfort

Make a master plan for every day:

In the beginning, which is the most difficult time because you will probably be hungry, put something, a no-calorie something, into your stomach every two hours or so. This will help. Your stomach cannot count calories. You are fooling yourself with low-calorie cranberry juice, diet Coke, a cup of tea, a cup of bouillon, a cup of clam juice, some chicken broth (fat-free, of course), a cup of cold consommé. If possible, plan your day around your diet. Have a cup of hot, hot coffee or your favorite tea to help you open your eyes and start the day. (I go down to the kitchen with my eyes closed; risky, but I can't face it otherwise.) Go out and get the paper; inspect the morning. Look at the diet. If you are cooking for others, too, decide what you will feed the nondieters. Some mornings your diet breakfast is better than others and you can serve the same breakfast to everyone—just vary the amounts.

In the middle of the morning stop what you are doing and have a drink of something: *something without calories*. Lunchtime approaches. Enjoy your lunch; eat it slowly, beside the fire, on the terrace or by the pool, but not, for heaven's sake, leaning over the kitchen sink. After lunch, if you are sedentary, take a walk. If you also have time to take a nap, do it; it helps to pass the time. Have another glass of low-calorie drink when you get up, or stop for tea in the midafternoon. Don't forget the slice of lemon for it. Lemon helps to give flavor and you can do without sugar.

Dinner is a real production. Concentrate on making a memorable meal, and don't just eat, DINE! Serve it in courses. Pretend you have an old-fashioned slow-moving butler, light the candles, turn on the hi-fi. Then take a short walk after dinner. If you have teenagers, they can do the dishes. If they won't (or if you don't have children), well, it won't hurt you. I remember that years ago when I was at school the girls who were trying to lose weight used to stand up for twenty minutes after each meal. Do you suppose it helped? Maybe it did, so that standing and washing dishes is a good thing.

Above all, and this is addressed to the older dieters, *do not lie in bed*. The most awful thing will happen—GAS, to be absolutely blunt. Therefore spend the evening doing something. Watching television is not recommended because so many of the commercials are concerned with food. This can lead to raiding the refrigerator, secret candy-eating; in short, the complete collapse of your will power. (My little old lady who hadn't eaten a pancake in fifty years nearly went off her head at the sight of a stack of Aunt Jemima's in glorious living color.)

Around nine or ten o'clock, have a low-calorie drink. It is especially nice if you are playing cards. Then before you go to bed, drink a glass of warm skim milk. You don't *like* it? All right, have it cold. Put some vanilla in it, add dash of Sucaryl, and put it in the blender to make it frothy. I know one gentleman who drinks a mixture of half club soda and half skim milk, and swears he likes it. This nightly glass of milk is very important. Even if its 60 calories or so puts your daily count over 600 you can wink an eye at this because milk is so essential to your well-being. Start drinking milk now, if you haven't before; you will be much better. My little old lady sometimes doesn't drink her milk at bedtime but puts it on her bedside table to have if she wakens in the middle of the night. It takes away that starving feeling, and helps you to have a good night's sleep.

DO NOT DESPAIR! When you hit a plateau and cannot lose an ounce no matter how good you have been, do not be desperate. Do not weigh yourself every day. Let the doctor do it when you visit him every week. You will soon discover that if you cheat, you will be found out. The scales do not lie. It is most embarrassing to be caught cheating and I want to save you. It is vitally important that you see your doctor regularly and that he should be aware of what you are doing. This is one diet he cannot pooh-pooh. He will end up being very proud of you, almost as if he had done this thing himself.

How to Use This Book

Now, just a word or two about this book. My observations of my own darling fat little old lady is that she doesn't like to work harder than she has to at anything. If it is something she doesn't want to do anyway, she just won't do it. Why do you suppose I counted all of these calories and carefully wrote down all the menus and recipes in the first place?

This book is divided into four sections, one for each season. For example: raspberries and fresh peaches in the summer; hot chowders and stews in the winter; clear jellied salads for the dog days are featured. When the menu calls for a special recipe —and there are lots of them—the recipe is right there on the page with the menu, or reference is given to the page on which it has already appeared. Nobody who is on a diet, all sad and mad and hungry, is going to look all through an index (although they *are* listed there, too). Nobody is going to count all those calories, either. Why should they? It is all done: each serving has its calorie content printed in front of it, and there is a total for each meal, and a grand total for the day. Some of the recipes are used more than once, but with different menus and appropriate page references given.

There is nothing boring about this diet. You are going to

learn to love the taste of real foods again, unmasked by butter, sauces, and cream. You are going to learn to cook in a new and different way. But best of all, you are going to feel better. The doctor will smile when he takes your blood pressure, the sales-lady at your favorite shop will automatically bring out all the smashing new clothes in size 12 and you won't have to deal with that cranky fitter anymore.

When the great day comes that your doctor agrees you may have more calories, merely adjust your portions. If he says 800 calories, we suggest that you add to the meat portion. Protein is so very important and unfortunately it is high in calories. Lots of people don't know this and think that steaks and chops are good diet food. This is not so. A calorie is a calorie is a calorie, and there is nowhere to hide from that basic fact.

When you have been on the 600-calorie diet for a short time your stomach will adjust to the smaller amounts of food you have been sending down to it. Don't increase your calories all at once when you reach your ideal weight. (I was extremely indiscreet last week with some French-fried eggplant. It tasted *heavenly*—and I was up all night with the galloping indiges-tion!) Save yourself from such troubles. Go slowly when you resume eating higher-calorie meals. Besides, you don't want to go through this diet all over again, do you?

Special Advice to the Cook

The kitchen equipment needed to turn out the 600-calorie diet is:

Teflon frying pan
Electric blender
Broiler
Measuring cup
Measuring spoons
Postal scales (you know, for weighing letters)

If you don't have this equipment, go and buy it immediately.

THE TEFLON PAN. Ignore all that advice about using low heat. You want the pan to get nice and black so that you can brown meat without using one speck of fat. Wash it, but don't try to scrub it out or you'll defeat your purpose.

THE BLENDER. This appliance makes life easier because you will no longer have to work foods through a sieve.

THE BROILER. This is a must to avoid frying.

THE MEASURING SPOONS AND CUP. Both are vital for self-evident reasons. When these recipes say ¼ cup of cottage cheese they don't mean take a guess.

THE POSTAL SCALE. Use it for weighing the allowed portions of meat. You will probably be surprised: Three lovely pieces of lean, fat-free corned beef weighing 3 ounces counts 180 calories.

While you are shopping look over the dietetic foods section of your store. If the one you patronize doesn't seem to have much variety, try another store for every day more and more foods are being prepared for the low-calorie diet and you will want a wide choice. If your town has a health food store, go in and look around. Most likely the proprietors of such a shop will be interested in your problem. Get into the habit of reading labels. Take a pocket magnifying glass along because the information you are seeking is always in very small print. It is there, though, so use it. Use dietetic salad dressings, dietetic fruit, dietetic gelatins, dietetic jams, dietetic chocolate syrup, even dietetic maple syrup. But be wary. Just because something says on the label in big print that it is low-calorie, don't believe it, until you read the fine print and find out how many calories there are and how large is the serving. Then draw your own conclusions.

Some of the dietetic foods may have to be doctored up a little, and I'll tell you how. Every calorie counts and you must save wherever you can. Use Sucaryl to sweeten what you want sweetened, if your doctor permits it. Don't say it is too much trouble. Nothing is too much trouble if it is going to make you look and feel better. If you stay on this diet *you will.*

A New Way of Cooking

Now that you are back in your kitchen with your new equipment and your diet foods, you must change your way of cooking. USE NO FAT. If even a teaspoon of fat is used it must be counted in the total calorie count for the day. Broil, bake, or poach, but NEVER FRY.

Presentation is half the battle. Never put a diet-sized portion on a great big dinner plate—it looks so pitiful. Use a salad plate, or one of your grandmother's pretty tea plates. A spray of watercress, a dusting of finely minced parsley, or a sprinkle of paprika adds no calories but does furnish a ton of eye appeal. Use your prettiest dishes, bring out your most unusual tablecloth. Serve the bouillon piping hot, it takes longer to eat. Eat your meal slowly. Dawdle. Serve the salad as a separate course. Don't have your coffee with dinner. Have it in the living room after you come in from your evening stroll, or after the dishes are done and the children are tucked into bed. Learn to enjoy what you are eating, and cook everything so beautifully that it will taste marvelous. My little old lady went to Maine Chance (you know, the beauty place); she lost only two pounds in two weeks. The 850 calories allowed each day was too much for her, but she came home raving about the food. Imagine, diet food so beautifully cooked and presented that every night was like a banquet! If you have someone to do the cooking (lucky you!) she will have to be carefully taught that she can't "slip a little butter on the green beans because they look so funny without it." It will be necessary to be adamant on this point, and some cooks are harder to convince than others. And watch out, if you cook for yourself, that *you* don't slip.

All of these menus were cooked either in the small kitchen of a Florida apartment or in my kitchen at home, using nothing more special than the equipment I have indicated. They were prepared by ordinary people. The basic recipes have come from everywhere, but they were changed, tailored, cut down and shaped and measured to our peculiar requirements. The entire family has enjoyed and benefited from the diet. My husband dislikes diet food as such. I wonder if he knows how much of it he has consumed in the past year? He is happy with his present waistline (36) although he refuses to give me any credit. The diet lunch at the Pancake House did it for him, he maintains. Ah, well—what he doesn't know hasn't hurt him in any way.

Now I want you girls, little old ladies, fellows, teenagers, fatties, to get down to business. Join us on the *The Adjustable Diet* and get rid of that UNSIGHTLY FAT.

The Secrets of Adjusting This Diet

In this section I am addressing myself to fatties with special problems. The career girls, the businessmen, the youngsters, teachers, students, and anyone else who needs help in adding or multiplying calories for the menus given in this book. Of course, it is easier to come home from the office and throw a little frozen package of macaroni and cheese in the oven, but it is also *fattening*.

Do your menu planning once a week. Just open the book and pick seven days. Make a marketing list. Cook at night. I know a very busy lady who does the week's cooking for herself and her husband on the weekend, then freezes it. She can come home at 5:30 from a meeting and have dinner ready in a matter of minutes.

If you are a working girl (or man), you should not try to go to the office each morning having had only four ounces of diet cranberry juice and black coffee. I know that there are lots of breakfasts in this book that give only that, but this is on the *600 calorie level* and, as I have explained frequently before, there are very few people who have to diet that stringently. Once again: ask your doctor what your calorie count should be. Read this book very carefully. You will see that 600 calories per day is recommended only in severe cases—sedentary people, people confined to bed or to a wheelchair, or people already under a doctor's care. Dr. Page, whose letter appears in the foreword, saw my mother every single week while she was on this 600 calorie diet. I am including a list of foods, with the calorie count, that may be added to the basic breakfast diet.

You must, of course, remember to add what you have eaten to the total count for the day. It is all right for you to write in the margin since this is your book. If you find you are not losing at a proper rate, you can consider what you have added and start subtracting. Learn to regard food with suspicion. Find out where the calories lurk. Above all, do not try to fool yourself into thinking that "just one slice of cake, or piece of pie, or pat of putter is not going to make any difference." It makes *all* the difference between losing weight and gaining weight.

Lunchtime and the Working Girl

There are both difficulties and pleasures when one lunches out. You must learn to tell the difference between fattening foods and foods that will help you to slim down. Almost any self-respecting restaurant has a chef's salad. Ask the waiter to serve the dressing separately and to bring you some lemon. Squeeze the lemon over the salad and add some pepper; forget the restaurant dressing. Try to avoid dessert. If you must have something, order sherbet. A grilled cheese sandwich will fill an aching void. A hamburger, without the roll, is good, and obtainable almost anywhere. Any kind of seafood salad, as long as it is not covered in mayonnaise, is an excellent low-calorie lunch. If you are serious about your diet, you will make a study of what is good for you and what isn't, and remember, if you are tempted to cheat, the only person you are cheating is yourself. Break the soda, sweet roll, and sundae habit.

The Lunch Box Brigade

There are more than schoolchildren in this brigade. Working girls and business executives, who can take their lunches to the office, card players who take a sandwich to the club, in fact, *anyone* who has occasion to pack a lunch is included. Thanks to the modern miracle of plastic wrap you can make Scandinavian-style sandwiches of one slice of bread, or no bread at all by using slices of cheese to hold the mustard and meat, or whatever. Look for those plastic boxes—"cold boxes" —that have hollow lids that contain distilled water. Place the lid in the freezer, and then whatever you place in the plastic box topped by the lid will remain cold until lunchtime—including yogurt, diet gelatin, fruit, or pudding. A wide-mouthed thermos bottle will hold a serving of leftover stew (the best kind), clear soup, a serving of diet clam chowder, or even your portion of canned soup, as indicated in the diet list. Celery, green pepper strips, carrots, or radishes will keep well wrapped in plastic wrap. If you must have dressing with your salad, put it in a tiny medicine bottle, take your greens in the cold box, and do the mixing at lunchtime. Put your mind to work on this problem and you will come up with lots of ideas to help you lose weight even while lunching.

The Businessman's Diet Lunch

Now we come to a real problem. There are only a few restaurants in this country that recognize the need to help the dieting businessman. There is a Pancake House near my husband's office that offers a "Diet Lunch." It consists of two small broiled hamburger patties, no roll, two slices of tomato, a lettuce leaf, half a canned peach with a spoonful of cottage cheese, and all the coffee you can drink. Boredom would set in very quickly for me, but, fortunately, my husband can eat the same thing for lunch, week in and week out.

If your man is truly interested in his diet, you can get him a pocket-sized calorie counter. Teach him to ask for meat that has been broiled. Have him develop the salad habit—even a regular salad with "real dressing" isn't as calorie-loaded as Lobster Newburg with rice. At Sardi's Restaurant in New York City, a place popular with actors (and are *they* figure conscious!), there is a different low-calorie lunch every day. In first-class restaurants the world over the usual portions are so large that one must train oneself to eat only half of what is served. This is difficult, but it can be done. If your overweight husband doesn't watch himself at lunch, you will be cooking diet dinners forever.

The Overweight Child

The overweight child can be a problem. It is vitally important that the child diet with the consent and under the supervision of your physician. There are many ways to substitute low-calorie foods for the fat-producing ones. Skim milk, diet gelatins and puddings, dietetic toppings, whipped butter or margarine are all available at the supermarket. Learn to find them and use them unobtrusively. Low-calorie soft drinks are a marvelous addition to our overfed world. Good for teeth, too. Teach your little dieter to ask for them at the soda counter after school. Teen-age girls are likely to starve themselves into shape and ruin their health at the same time. So, Mothers, keep a close check on them even if they do think you are "square."

How to Adjust the Diet to the Individual

Since every single item listed in this book has a calorie count printed in front of it, you will not have a very difficult time finding out what things can be safely increased, and

where the calories are hiding. For example, the items added
to the day's menu below are printed in italics.

TOTAL CALORIES FOR THE DAY: 1,284, INCLUDING
58 OF SNACKS

334	*Breakfast*	242	*Lunch*	708	*Dinner*
12	½ cup diet cranberry juice	60	½ can chicken noodle soup	200	*2 martinis on the rocks*
50	½ cup cream of wheat cereal	*34*	*2 saltines*	30	tomato madrilene
		60	a whole orange	190	chicken in red wine
22	2 oz. skim milk	*88*	*1 glass skim milk*	60	asparagus with water chestnuts
150	*English muffin*		Midafternoon tea	100	½ cup boiled rice
100	*1 Tbs. butter*			20	cucumber and onion salad
00	black coffee			50	chocolate pot de crème
	Midmorning drink			58	6 oz. skim milk at bedtime

Things to Add to Vary Breakfasts

Breads

Bagel, 1 medium	110
Baking powder biscuits, 2 small	109
Boston brown bread, 3″ x ½″ piece	75
Bran muffin	100
Corn bread, 2″ square	200
Cracked wheat bread, 1 slice, ½″ thick	60
Date and nut bread, 1 slice	90
English muffin, toasted	150
Pepperidge Farm, white, 1 slice	63
Pepperidge Farm, whole wheat, 1 slice	45
Thomas' Protein bread, 1 slice	40
Rye bread, 1 slice	75

Cereals

All Bran, 8 oz.	100
40% Bran Flakes, ¾ cup	97
Cheerios, 1⅛ cups	104
Corn Flakes, 1⅓ cups	110
Grapenuts, ⅜ cup	112
Kix, 1 cup	92
Rice Flakes, 1 cup	115
Rice Krispies, 1 cup	108
Puffed Rice, 1 cup	55
Sugar Crisps, ¾ cup	110
Puffed Wheat, 1 cup	50

Wheat Germ, ¾ cup	185
Wheaties, 1 cup	105

Meats

Bacon, broiled, 2 strips	95
Chipped beef, 6 thin slices	150
Corned beef hash, canned, 3 oz.	180

Miscellaneous

Butter, 1 Tbs.	100
Cruller, 1 medium	150
Danish pastry, 1 small	139
Egg, with nothing added	70
Holland Rusk, 1 piece	61
Honey, 1 Tbs.	62
Melba Toast, 1 slice	30

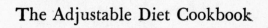

The Adjustable Diet Cookbook

WINTER MENUS

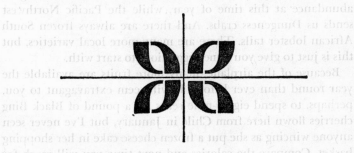

Many times the end of our "weight rope" is reached after the winter holidays. We have partied, eating and drinking much too much for several months. The budget has shrunk and we are overstuffed. With New Year's Day come the resolutions: Save money, get some sleep, lose some weight, go on the wagon, stop smoking. Many people can lose weight merely by cutting out alcohol; just that, nothing else. It is terribly difficult to lose weight while continuing to imbibe several drinks every day. Alcohol contains CALORIES—useless, harmful calories, 100 in every ounce. Paint 100 on your cocktail glass with red nail polish as a nasty little reminder for yourself each time you reach for a drink. Be of good cheer, however. The spirit of the season is with you. With any luck you can hold out until Lent begins and you will have a new chance to reresolve to do all things you have slipped up on since the first of the year.

1

There are gastronomic delights for the dieter in the dead of winter. Fish, that marvelous aid to the overweight, is available at your nearest fish market. Now that we have the wonder of frozen foods, even the most landlocked American can choose from a great variety of seafood. Florida red snapper is delicious, drizzled with white wine and lightly, oh, *very lightly,* spread with butter or margarine and broiled. Bay scallops have a flavor all their own, and winter is their own special season. If you live near New York you can probably have magnificent striped bass, sea squab (inelegantly known as Atlantic blowfish), and mussels. Californians can get Pacific rex sole, Pacific rockfish, and spiny lobster. Chicagoans find lake herring in abundance at this time of year, while the Pacific Northwest sends us Dungeness crabs. And there are always frozen South African lobster tails. There are many more local varieties, but this is just to give you some suggestions to start with.

Because of the airplane, many more fruits are available the year round than ever before. It will seem extravagant to you, perhaps, to spend eighty-nine cents for a pound of Black Bing cherries flown here from Chile in January, but I've never seen anyone wincing as she put a frozen cheese cake in her shopping basket. Compare the calories and next time you will reach for the cherries. Grapefruit is at its peak in the winter months, pineapples from Puerto Rico abound; Mexican cantaloupes, winter pears, strawberries from California and Florida, the first hothouse rhubarb, and countless others are to be found in almost any supermarket. Apples are at their peak and reasonably priced. Vegetables loom large in any balanced diet, giving vitamins and variety to your winter meals. California supplies artichokes—low in calories, delightful to eat; and there are broccoli, Brussels sprouts, beets, and green beans, too. Cabbage, eggplant, cauliflower, celery, onions, parsnips, turnips are in the shops and all kinds of southern greens—collards, mustard greens, kale, turnip greens, and good old reliable spinach—are at greengrocers. In addition you are offered squash and mushrooms, carrots and kohlrabi—surely there must be something here that will appeal to you?

Salad, the staple of the dedicated dieter, is readily available

in winter, thanks again to our wonderful transportation sys-
tem. Cucumbers are available year round; lettuce, escarole,
chicory, Belgian endives can be found anywhere. And have
you ever tried Chinese cabbage? Chives are found in the frozen-
food compartment, bunches of fresh parsley are easily come by.
You may have to order watercress especially from your produce
man, but it makes so much difference in how your diet food
looks (it tastes crisp and spicy as well) that it is worth the
effort.

Stews, ragouts, and goulashes warm your heart as well as
your tummy, they also help the budget. A simple pot roast,
herb-broiled chicken, or beef bourguignon will be most welcome after all the rich holiday fare you have consumed, and
low-caloried recipes make them all the more acceptable.

Winter Menus

Main dishes for dinner

❧ WEEK 1 ❧

Beef stew
Lobster
Shashlik
Stuffed green pepper
Filet of beef
Roast beef
Chicken Charlotte

❧ WEEK 2 ❧

Lamb chop
Lobster Cantonese
Meat loaf
Stone crab
Lasagna
Corned beef
Scallops

❧ WEEK 3 ❧

Roast pork
Broiled chicken

Calves' liver
Veal scaloppini
Rock Cornish game hen
Chinese shrimp
Chile con carne

WEEK 4

Boiled beef
Clams casino
Chicken in red wine
Finnan haddie
Leg of lamb
Chicken livers Victor Hugo
Chili beefsteak

WEEK 5

Curried lamb
Shad roe sauté
Calves' liver en brochette
Filet of sole Veronique
London broil
Eggplant Parmigiana
Beef tongue

WEEK 6

Pot roast
Cabbage rolls
Chicken Marengo
Sweetbreads in wine
Crabmeat creole
Swedish meatballs
Scampi

TOTAL CALORIES FOR THE DAY: 649, INCLUDING 60 OF SNACKS

120	*Breakfast*	189	*Lunch*	280	*Dinner*
50	½ grapefruit	20	Clear chicken broth	200	Beef stew with vegetables [made the previous day]*
70	1 soft-boiled egg Black coffee	20	Cucumber and onion salad*		
		34	2 Venus wafers	35	Endive with low-calorie dressing
1	Midmorning bouillon	115	Baked rice pudding* Tea with lemon		
				45	½ cup diet peaches Black coffee
		1	Midafternoon snack		
				58	6 oz. warm skim milk at bedtime

CUCUMBER AND ONION SALAD

☞ Slice cucumbers and onions very thin. Sprinkle with dill weed and salt and coarse black pepper. Cover with white vinegar. Chill before serving.

BAKED RICE PUDDING

Serves 6. Calories per serving: 115. (Give some to the neighbors.) ■ *Preheat oven to 300 degrees F.*

1 qt. skim milk	½ tsp. salt
1 tsp. liquid Sucaryl	½ tsp. nutmeg
½ cup raw rice	1 tsp. vanilla

☞ In slightly greased 1½-quart casserole combine all ingredients. Bake uncovered, stirring frequently the first hour. This takes 2½ hours to cook and turns out just like the Poor Man's Rice Pudding Mama used to make when she was thin and poor and young.

BEEF STEW

Serves 3.   Calories per serving: 200.   ■   *Make the day before.*

1 lb. beef round, cubed	½ tsp. salt
2 cups red wine	¼ tsp. pepper
½ cup celery, chopped	3 carrots, sliced
½ cup carrots, chopped	3 small onions
½ cup green pepper, chopped	3 small stalks celery
½ cup onion, chopped	Parsley, chopped
1 clove garlic, pressed	

☞ Brown the beef in the Teflon pan. No fat, no flour needed—it will brown. Remove browned meat to Dutch oven. Rinse Teflon pan with some of the red wine to the glaze. Put all the vegetables into the pan with the meat, salt, and pepper and let cook gently for several hours until the meat is tender and the vegetables seem to have melted together. Put in refrigerator. When cold, remove every speck of fat that has risen to the top and solidified. Add 2 sliced carrots, 3 small onions, and 3 small stalks of celery. Simmer for about 30 minutes, add a little pepper, and serve from a casserole with chopped parsley sprinkled over the top.

☞ Don't forget your diet drinks and your warm milk at bedtime.

TOTAL CALORIES FOR THE DAY: 605, INCLUDING 60 OF SNACKS

97	*Breakfast*	223	*Lunch*	225	*Dinner*
25	½ cup V-8 juice	100	1 slice calves'	100	Broiled live
50	½ cup Cream of		liver* with		lobster
	Wheat	30	1 slice bacon	25	Broiled tomato
22	2 oz. skim milk		and sliced	20	Asparagus
	Black coffee		onion	20	Mixed green
		50	Grapefruit		salad
1	Midmorning		sections on	60	Orange
	low-calorie		watercress		zabaglione*
	drink		Tea with		Black coffee
			lemon		
		43	Diet pears	58	6 oz. warm skim
					milk
		1	Midafternoon		
			drink		

CALVES' LIVER

Serves 1.   Calories per serving: 100.

☞ Fry the bacon in the Teflon pan. Pour off the grease. Let the bacon drain on a paper towel. Sauté the onion in the pan and then the liver—very quickly so the liver won't be tough. Makes all the difference.

LOBSTER: Just a reminder—*no butter!* My little lady likes to dip her lobster in vinegar. I am partial to lemon juice. Bet you don't remember how good lobster tastes all by itself.

When you broil the tomato, put some chopped parsley and onion and a pinch of Parmesan cheese on top with salt and pepper.

ORANGE ZABAGLIONE

Serves 3.   Calories per serving: 60.

| 3 egg yolks | ½ cup orange juice |
| ½ tsp. Sucaryl | ¼ tsp. almond extract |

☞ Place egg yolks in the top of a double boiler. Add Sucaryl and beat with an eggbeater until mixture is thick and lemon-colored. Place over hot water (do not allow the bottom of the pan to touch the water). Add the almond extract and orange juice slowly, continue beating until the mixture has the consistency of heavy cream. Remove from heat and chill. Serve cold in sherbet glasses.

TOTAL CALORIES FOR THE DAY: 586, INCLUDING 60 OF SNACKS

166	*Breakfast*	104	*Lunch*	256	*Dinner*
50	½ grapefruit	95	Shrimp salad*	175	Shashlik*
70	1 poached egg		with lots of	25	Broccoli
	on		radishes and	35	Sliced orange
46	Gluten toast		cucumbers		on red onion
	Black coffee	9	Lime D-Zerta		salad
1	low-calorie		Tea with	26	Jellied prune
	drink in		lemon		whip*
	midmorning				Black coffee
		1	midafternoon	58	6 oz. skim milk
			drink		at bedtime

SHRIMP SALAD

Serves 1.   Calories per serving: 95.   ■   *8 average shrimp with as many radishes and cucumber slices as you want.*   ■   *Mix with 2 teaspoons diet mayonnaise thinned with lemon juice.*

SHASHLIK

Calories per serving: 175.

☞ My little old lady has some very attractive skewers; this really dresses up a meal that starts as a broiled chop. How boring can you be? Early in the day make a marinade of diet Italian dressing with quite a bit of lemon juice. Cut very lean lamb from the leg or from the middle of the double lamb chop. Be very careful to remove all fat. Make 6 bite-size pieces per serving: 2 ounces. Weigh it on the little scale. Marinate the lamb until just before time to cook it. Drain the meat on paper towel—even diet dressing harbors those dratted calories. Cut green peppers in inch squares. Alternate these, whole mushrooms, cherry tomatoes, and small cooked white onions on the skewers and broil until the meat is brown (not burned), turning frequently.

JELLIED PRUNE WHIP

Serves 4. Calories per serving: about 26.

☞ Dissolve contents of envelope of orange-flavor D-Zerta in 1 cup boiling water. Chill until slightly thickened. Set bowl in ice and water, beat until fluffy and thick. Beat 1 egg white into soft peaks and add to mixture. Fold into beaten mixture a small jar of baby-food puréed prunes. Chill until firm.

TOTAL CALORIES FOR THE DAY: 647½, INCLUDING 60 OF SNACKS

50	*Breakfast*	162½	*Lunch*	375	*Dinner*
50	½ melon	12½	No-account	295	Stuffed green
	Black coffee		borscht*		pepper*
1	Midmorning	150	½ of a 3-egg	25	Yellow squash
	snack		omelet	25	Mixed green
			Tea with		salad
			lemon	30	Almond rennet
		1	Midafter-		custard
			noon drink		Black coffee
				58	6 oz. warm skim
					milk at
					bedtime

NO-ACCOUNT BORSCHT

Makes 4 cups. Calories per serving: 12½.

VEGETABLE STOCK

½ cup onions, chopped
½ cup cabbage, chopped
2 cups celery with leaves,
   chopped
6 peppercorns

2 cups tomato juice
1 tsp. Savita (from the health
   food store)
4 cups water
Dash of paprika

☞ No calories when strained; makes 6 to 8 cups. Place the chopped or diced vegetables together with the tomato juice in a medium-size covered soup pot. Dissolve the Savita in 4 cups of water and add. Simmer covered for 1 hour. Add other seasonings and simmer for 10 minutes more. Serve hot as a vegetable soup. For stock, strain, cool, and store in a covered jar in the refrigerator.

BORSCHT

4 cups vegetable stock	2 Tbs. lemon juice
½ cup grated raw beets	

☞ To the four cups of vegetable stock add grated beets and lemon juice. Cook, covered, for 15 minutes. Cool and chill in the refrigerator.

STUFFED GREEN PEPPERS

Serves 3.   Calories per serving: 295.

3 uniform green peppers	½ Tbs. margarine or butter
1½ onions, chopped	½ of a #2½ can of tomatoes
3 oz. cooked meat or	Beef bone
hamburger, lean	Pepper
1 Tbs. uncooked rice	2 Tbs. lemon juice
Pepper and salt	½ Tbs. brown sugar
½ of 1 beaten egg	½ tsp. Sucaryl
1 Tbs. cold water	

☞ Ask the butcher for a beef bone. Wash the peppers. Cut a 1-inch piece from the stem ends and save. Carefully scoop out seeds and fiber. Chop 1 onion and mix with meat, rice, pepper, salt, egg, and water. Stuff the peppers with this mixture. Replace top firmly. Melt margarine in Dutch oven and sauté remaining onion for 5 minutes. Add tomatoes, the bone, more pepper. Arrange the peppers in an upright position. Cover and cook for 1¼ hours over low heat. Stir in the lemon juice, brown sugar, and Sucaryl. Cook 15 minutes more.

TOTAL CALORIES FOR THE DAY: 599, INCLUDING
59 OF SNACKS

	Breakfast		*Lunch*		*Dinner*
67		110		363	
12	4 oz. diet cranberry juice	60	Boston clam chowder*	250	Broiled filet of beef*
45	1 slice gluten toast	50	½ grapefruit Tea with lemon	40	Sautéed green pepper*
10	Diet jam Black coffee			25	Turnip greens
1	Midmorning drink		Midafternoon tea	15	Watercress salad
				33	Coffee mousse* Black coffee
				58	6 oz. skim milk at bedtime

CLAM CHOWDER

Serves 6. Calories per serving: 60. May be frozen.

1 10½ oz. can of clams (save the juice)
1 medium onion, chopped
¼ cup carrots, diced

½ cup tomato juice
¼ tsp. white pepper
2 cup skim milk

☞ Put ½ cup clam liquid into a saucepan, then everything, except clams and milk. Cook, covered, over low heat for 20 minutes, or until the vegetables are tender. Cut the clams in halves and add to the saucepan. Add the milk gradually, stirring constantly. Simmer for 5 minutes. Garnish with chopped parsley.

FILET OF BEEF

This is the night to have a party. Then you may have a whole filet and roast it. Your share is 4 ounces—250 calories. Serve it rare. If you're not having a party have the butcher slice off 4 ounces for you, and broil it. Not nearly as much fun.

SAUTÉED GREEN PEPPER

Serves 3. Calories per serving: 40.

Trace of olive oil in Teflon pan
1 onion, sliced
1 green pepper, sliced
¼ lb. mushrooms, sliced
Pinch of crushed red pepper
Pinch of oregano

☞ Heat the skillet and sauté the onion 5 minutes. Add the pepper and sauté 3 minutes. Stir frequently. Add the mushrooms, red pepper, and oregano. Cook over medium heat for 5 minutes. Keep stirring.

COFFEE MOUSSE

Serves 8. Calories per serving: 33. And no one will ever know.

¼ cup cold water
1 tsp. gelatin
4 tsps. instant coffee
2 tsps. Sucaryl
½ cup boiling water
½ cup ice water
½ cup non-fat dried milk

☞ Combine ¼ cup cold water, the gelatin, instant coffee (Sanka, if you must), and Sucaryl in a small pan. Add ½ cup boiling water; stir until dissolved. Cool until slightly set, like soft jelly. Whip ½ cup ice water with ½ cup dried non-fat milk until thick. Blend into cool coffee solution while beating at high speed. Chill until set. Serve in parfait glasses.

TOTAL CALORIES FOR THE DAY: 636, INCLUDING 59 OF SNACKS

	105 *Breakfast*		125 *Lunch*		347 *Dinner*
70	1 poached egg on	60	Mulligataw-ney*	240	3 oz. lean roast beef
35	Protegen toast Black coffee	65	1 small apple Tea with lemon	40	3 glazed onions*
1	Midmorning low-calorie drink		Midafternoon tea	20	Spinach
				15	Mixed green salad
				32	Apricot whip* Black coffee
				58	6 oz. skim milk at bedtime

MULLIGATAWNEY

Serves 8.   Calories per serving: 60. Can be frozen.

1 large chicken breast	Pinch of mace
1 Tbs. cooking oil	2 sprigs parsley
¼ cup carrot, chopped	1 tsp. parsley
¼ cup green pepper, chopped	1 tsp. salt
1 onion, peeled and diced	Pinch of pepper
1 tart apple, diced	1 1-lb. can tomatoes
5 cups hot water in which 3	¼ tsp. Sucaryl
chicken bouillon cubes	½ tsp. curry powder
have been dissolved	
2 whole cloves	

☞ Heat the oil in a soup pot. Add the carrot, green pepper, onion, and apple and sauté over low heat for 15 minutes. Add the hot water with cubes and all remaining ingredients. Cover and simmer for 1 hour. Remove the chicken. Cut the meat into small pieces and return to the pot after you have discarded the skin and bones. Serve in soup plates. Can be frozen.

GLAZED ONIONS

3 onions per serving: 40 calories.

3 small onions	**1 tsp. brown sugar**
1 cup chicken broth	**¼ Tbs. Worcestershire sauce**

☞ Combine all ingredients in saucepan. Cook over low heat for 20 minutes or until the onions are tender and the sauce almost absorbed.

APRICOT WHIP

Serves 3.   Calories per serving: 32.

☞ Dissolve contents of an envelope of orange-flavor D-Zerta in ½ cup boiling water. Drain 1 can (8 oz.) dietetic apricot halves. Add ½ cup of the liquid to hot mixture with 1½ teaspoons lemon juice and ¼ teaspoon rum. Chill until slightly thickened. Place in a bowl of ice and water. Beat with chilled rotary beater until fluffy and thick. Chop apricots fine and fold in. Chill in individual molds until firm.

TOTAL CALORIES FOR THE DAY: 644, INCLUDING 59 OF SNACKS

70	*Breakfast*	125	*Lunch*	390	*Dinner*
50	½ cup Cream of Wheat	75	Artichoke vinaigrette*	220	Chicken Charlotte*
20	¼ cup skim milk Black coffee	50	½ grapefruit Tea with lemon	23	½ cup broccoli
				27	½ cup carrots
1	Midmorning bouillon			20	Mixed green salad with diet dressing
				100	Caramel custard* Black coffee
				58	6 oz. skim milk at bedtime

ARTICHOKE VINAIGRETTE

2 tsps. lemon juice with ½ onion and some celery

☞ Soak artichoke in salted water for 1 hour. Cook 45 minutes. To make the dressing dilute Italian Diet dressing with fresh lemon juice, to taste. Then chop, very, very fine a carrot, an onion, parsley, and the outside (the red part) of 3 or 4 radishes. Add 1 teaspoon of fresh horseradish and ½ teaspoon of mustard. Some people like to add a finely chopped gherkin. Sprinkle well with paprika and combine with the dressing.

CHICKEN CHARLOTTE

1 chicken, quartered	1 Tbs. chopped chutney
1 Tbs. butter	1 Tbs. sliced almonds
Salt and pepper	½ tsp. cinnamon
1 cup of liquid from diet	½ tsp. curry powder
pack Mandarin oranges	¼ tsp. thyme
1 Tbs. raisins	½ cup Mandarin oranges

☞ Arrange chicken quarters in a greased shallow baking dish. Dot with butter. Sprinkle with salt and pepper. Bake at 425 degrees for 15 minutes or until golden brown. Meanwhile, in a sauce pan combine the rest of the ingredients. Simmer for 10 minutes. Pour sauce over browned chicken. Bake at 350 degrees for 1 hour or until chicken is tender. No one will believe it is diet chicken. So don't tell them.

CARAMEL CUSTARD

Serves 4. Calories per serving: 100.

2 tsps. liquid Sucaryl	1 tsp. vanilla
2 cups skim milk	4 tsps. brown sugar
3 eggs, lightly beaten	Nutmeg, if desired

☞ In blender (If you don't have one, buy one immediately!) add the Sucaryl to 2 cups skim milk. Add 3 beaten eggs. Add vanilla. Blend at low speed for 30 seconds. Put 1 teaspoon brown sugar into the bottom of each of four custard cups. Pour mixture carefully into each cup. Now sprinkle with nutmeg, if you want it. Place filled cups in a pan of hot water, having water come to within ½ inch of the tops of the cups. Bake in a slow oven (300 degrees) for 1 hour or until a knifeblade comes out clean. Refrigerate immediately. Serve cold.

TOTAL CALORIES FOR THE DAY: 589, INCLUDING
60 OF SNACKS

50 *Breakfast*	134 *Lunch*	345 *Dinner*
50 ½ cup orange juice	55 ½ can tomato soup, diluted with water	200 Broiled lamb chop
Black coffee		35 Carrots
	34 2 Venus wafers	35 Coleslaw
1 Midmorning drink	45 Diet peaches	75 Orange ice
	Tea with lemon	Black coffee
	1 Midafternoon drink	58 6 oz. warm skim milk at bedtime

LAMB CHOP: Remove all visible fat before cooking.

The lamb chop should be broiled; the carrots are plain, boiled. Sprinkle them with chopped mint, before serving.

For the coleslaw, cut your cabbage fine, using a grater, a knife, or one of those slicers. Marzetti's in Columbus has an absolutely delicious coleslaw dressing, and now those wonderful people have come up with a low-calorie dressing that I can't tell from the regular stuff. Find it, or write to them in Columbus, Ohio.

You can use commercial orange ice, but if you do, give yourself only 3 ounces.

TOTAL CALORIES FOR THE DAY: 593, INCLUDING
59 OF SNACKS

120	*Breakfast*	64	*Lunch*	350	*Dinner*
50	½ cup grape-fruit juice	30	Marinated green beans in lettuce cup	185	Lobster Cantonese*
70	1 scrambled egg*	25	2 Tbs. cottage cheese	100	½ cup rice
	Black coffee			15	Watercress salad
1	Midmorning drink	9	Lime D-Zerta Tea with lemon	50	½ cantaloupe with fresh lime
			Midafternoon tea		Black coffee
				58	6 oz. skim milk at bedtime

SCRAMBLED EGG

☞ Use your Teflon pan to scramble the egg.

The green beans can be marinated in diet French dressing.

LOBSTER CANTONESE

Serves 3. Calories per serving: 185.

½ Tbs. cooking oil
1 clove garlic, peeled and
   minced
½ cup water chestnuts, sliced
½ cup bamboo shoots, cut up
1 rounded Tbs. chives
1 rounded Tbs. coarsely
   grated carrot

1 cup hot water with chicken
   bouillon cube
1 Tbs. cornstarch
1 Tbs. soy sauce
1 lb. cooked lobster meat cut
   in small chunks
Salt, pepper, and MSG to
   taste   [continued]

☞ Heat the oil in a large heavy skillet or wok. What's a wok? A round bottomed Chinese pan. Very useful. Sauté the garlic, water chestnuts, bamboo shoots, chives, and carrot over low heat for 15 minutes. Add the chicken bouillon and cook 5 minutes. Blend the cornstarch with soy sauce to dissolve and stir into skillet. Stir vigorously and cook slowly until thickened. Add the lobster meat and stir into the sauce until heated through. Season to taste. Serve over steamed rice.

TOTAL CALORIES FOR THE DAY: 591, INCLUDING 59 OF SNACKS

	65 *Breakfast*		118 *Lunch*		349 *Dinner*
45	1 slice gluten toast	20	2 Diet-10 crackers	290	Meat loaf*
				15	Mushrooms
20	½ cup Mott's 5 Fruit (dietetic) drink	55	½ can Campbell's chicken soup with rice	22	Zucchini
				15	Cucumber salad
	Black coffee			7	Lime chiffon*
1	Midmorning low-calorie drink	43	½ cup diet peaches		Black coffee
			Tea with lemon	58	6 oz. skim milk at bedtime
			Midafternoon tea		

MEAT LOAF

Serves 6.   Calories per serving: 290.

1½ pounds ground lean beef chuck or round	¼ tsps. pepper
2 Tbs. ice water	3 Tbs. grated onion
1 egg beaten	1 Tbs. dried breadcrumbs
3 Tbs. ketchup	1 tsp. salad oil
1½ tsps. salt	3 Tbs. chili sauce

☞ Mix together the beef, ice water, egg, ketchup, salt, pepper, onion, breadcrumbs. Shape into a loaf and place in a lightly oiled bakingpan or pack into a lightly oiled 8 inch loaf pan. Bake in a 375 degree oven 30 minutes. Spread chili sauce on top and bake 30 more minutes. Let stand for 20 minutes after removing from the oven and it will slice easier. You can serve the mushrooms, sliced, and cooked with a little water in the Teflon pan with the meat until limp. Or broil them. No butter, though.

LIME CHIFFON

Makes 4 servings, about 7 calories each.

☞ Dissolve contents of 1 envelope of D-Zerta Lime in 1 cup of boiling water. Add enough Sucaryl, equal to 2 teaspoons sugar, chill until slightly thickened. Place bowl in larger bowl of ice and water. Whip with rotary beater until fluffy. Fold in 1 egg white, beaten to soft peaks. Pour into sherbet glasses and chill until firm.

TOTAL CALORIES FOR THE DAY: 499, INCLUDING 58 OF SNACKS:

82	*Breakfast*	157	*Lunch*	202	*Dinner*
12	½ cup diet cranberry juice	84	7 oz. cream of celery soup	100	¾ cup stone crab
		30	2 Ry-Krisp	17	½ cup asparagus
70	Soft-boiled egg Black coffee	43	½ cup diet apricots Tea with lemon	35	Red-and-white coleslaw
	Midmorning drink			50	½ grapefruit Black coffee
				58	6 oz. skim milk at bedtime

☞ This is a lazy day, nothing difficult to prepare. You can get the stone crab, already cooked, from your fish market. You feel as if you have had a lot to eat because you have to take all that time getting it out of the shell.

Use diet salad dressing, red cabbage and white cabbage.

TOTAL CALORIES FOR THE DAY: 658, INCLUDING
59 OF SNACKS

	Breakfast		Lunch		Dinner
104	*Breakfast*	205	*Lunch*	290	*Dinner*
27	½ cup fresh	135	Cheese soufflé*	220	Lasagna*
	strawberries	20	Cucumber and	20	½ cup broccoli
	on		watercress	15	Salad with lots
55	½ cup		salad		of radishes
	cornflakes	50	1 small orange	35	Spiced fruit*
22	2 oz. skim milk		Tea with lemon		Black coffee
	Black coffee				
			Midafternoon	58	6 oz. skim milk
1	Midmorning		tea		at bedtime
	drink				

CHEESE SOUFFLÉ

Serves 3.   Calories per serving: 135.

1 Tbs. margarine or butter	3 eggs, separated
1 Tbs. flour	1 tsp. dried mustard
1 cup skim milk	
3 oz. grated cheese—American,	
Parmesan, Swiss, whatever	

☞ Melt margarine, add flour and milk to make a cream
sauce. Add cheese. Add egg yolks. Mix well. Beat egg whites
until stiff and fold into cheese mixture. Place in soufflé dish
and bake 45 minutes to 1 hour in 350-degree oven. Serve at
once.

[*continued*]

LASAGNA

Serves 3.   Calories per serving: 220.

⅓ lb. chopped meat
½ onion, peeled and chopped
1 clove garlic
¼ can tomato paste
2 oz. hot water
1 #2 can Italian plum
   tomatoes

FILLING

½ lb. Buitoni lasagna noodles
¼ cup grated Parmesan cheese
¼ cup cubed Mozzarella cheese
¾ lb. Ricotta cheese

☞ Mix beef with onion and garlic. Brown in Teflon pan. Blend the tomato paste with hot water in large saucepan. Add plum tomatoes and meat mixture and boil rapidly for 3 minutes. Lower the heat and simmer for 1 hour. Cook noodles as directed on package. Drain well. Pour a little of the sauce into an 8-by-10-inch baking dish. Over this place a layer of noodles, a layer of grated cheese, a layer of sauce, a layer of Mozzarella and a tablespoon of Ricotta dotted about. You should end with the top layer of sauce, sprinkled with Parmesan. Bake in a 350-degree oven for about 30 minutes, or until the lasagna is bubbling. Let stand for 5 or 10 minutes before serving.

SPICED FRUIT

Serves 3.   Calories per serving: 35.

½ can dietetic pears with
   liquid
½ can water-packed sour red
   cherries, drained
½ cup dietetic apricot halves
¼ cup water

1 tsp. Sucaryl
½ tsp. ground ginger
1 cinnamon stick
2 whole cloves
Juice of 1 lemon

☞ Place fruit in large pan. Mix water, Sucaryl, lemon juice, ginger, and pear liquid and pour into pan. Add cinnamon sticks and cloves. Simmer 5 minutes, basting. Let cool in liquid, strain out spices, and pour over fruit.

TOTAL CALORIES FOR THE DAY: 555, INCLUDING 59 OF SNACKS

	Breakfast		Lunch		Dinner
37	*Breakfast*	109	*Lunch*	350	*Dinner*
12	½ cup diet cranberry juice	100	Large artichoke vinaigrette (page 18)	200	4 oz. corned beef
				25	1 cup cabbage
35	1 slice Protegen toast with low-calorie jam Black coffee	9	Orange D-Zerta Tea with lemon	50	Small boiled potato
			Midafternoon tea	20	Mixed green salad
				75	Fresh strawberries Black coffee
1	Midmorning drink			58	6 oz. warm skim milk at bedtime

NEW ENGLAND BOILED DINNER

This is another easy meal that tastes wonderful. Have you ever put mustard on a boiled potato? You'll never miss the butter.

Put piece of corned beef, all visible fat removed, into large pot. Cover with water. Add 1 sliced onion, and 10 peppercorns. Simmer for several hours until tender.

Cook the vegetables in the water the corned beef was cooked in.

Save a few strawberries for tomorrow's lunch.

TOTAL CALORIES FOR THE DAY: 595, INCLUDING 60 OF SNACKS

90 *Breakfast*	150 *Lunch*	295 *Dinner*
50 ½ grapefruit	100 Steamed clams	150 Scallops in
35 1 slice Protegen	with broth*	white wine*
toast with	50 Fruit salad*	25 Baked tomato
5 Diet plum	with 2 tsps.	25 Spinach
preserve	cottage	20 Mixed green
Black coffee	cheese	salad
	Tea with lemon	75 Fresh
1 Midmorning		pineapple
drink	1 Midafternoon	Black coffee
	drink	
		58 6 oz. warm skim
		milk at
		bedtime

STEAMED CLAMS WITH BROTH

☞ Scrub your steamers to a fare-thee-well to get rid of the sand. Four ounces of clams sans shell is 90 calories, and that's quite a few clams. We served ours with a cup of broth and there was the little old lady again, dipping hers in vinegar. Put the clams into a large deep kettle with some water, cover, bring to a boil, and cook over low heat until the clams are all open. Strain the broth through cheesecloth and serve in cups.

FRUIT SALAD

☞ Cut a fresh pineapple in half, lengthwise. Carefully cut out pulp and reserve for the dessert for dinner. In one half of the pineapple shell place two teaspoons of cottage cheese, two grapefruit sections, three grapes, two orange sections, and a couple of pieces of pineapple. Decorate the top with some strawberries saved from last night's dinner; stick in a piece of fresh mint; and serve with a flourish.

SCALLOPS IN WHITE WINE

Serves 3. Calories per serving: 150.

¾ lb. scallops	¼ lb. mushrooms, chopped
1 tsp. salt	1 Tbs. parsley, chopped
¼ tsp. freshly ground black pepper	3 Tbs. dry white wine
	3 tsps. butter or margarine

☞ Wash and drain scallops. If you are lucky enough to have bay scallops, leave them whole. If you are using sea scallops, quarter them. Arrange the scallops in three shells or baking dishes; sprinkle with salt, pepper, and mushrooms. Sprinkle with parsley. Use 1 tablespoon of wine for each shell. Dot with butter or margarine. Bake in a 450-degree oven for 10 minutes. Serve with a wedge of lemon.

TOTAL CALORIES FOR THE DAY: 588, INCLUDING
60 OF SNACKS

35	*Breakfast*	144	*Lunch*	349	*Dinner*
35	½ cup diet applesauce	10	Chicken broth	285	3 oz. roast pork tenderloin*
	Black coffee	75	Shirred egg*		
1	Midmorning drink	14	1 piece Melba toast	40	1 cup turnips, mashed
		45	½ cup canned diet pears	15	½ cup mustard greens
		1	Midafternoon drink	9	Lemon D-Zerta Black coffee
				58	6 oz. warm skim milk at bedtime

SHIRRED EGG

☞ What could be easier? Wipe the inside of a shirred-egg dish with a piece of paper towel that has a little butter on it, just to make the egg slide. Break the egg in carefully; sprinkle with pepper and salt. Bake in a 350-degree oven for 10 minutes, or until the egg is set. Serve in the dish. Garnish with a piece of parsley. (It doesn't look so lonesome that way.)

ROAST TENDERLOIN OF PORK

☞ This happened by accident. In the freezer at the little old lady's there was a little tenderloin of pork, and she just loves pork. We roasted it after rubbing it tenderly with rosemary and salt and pepper, sliced it very thin, then weighed it on the little scale. It tasted just marvelous. You see, this diet isn't so bad!

TOTAL CALORIES FOR THE DAY: 638, INCLUDING 60 OF SNACKS

	Breakfast		Lunch		Dinner
85	*Breakfast*	138	*Lunch*	355	*Dinner*
50	½ cup orange juice	80	Deviled egg*	200	Broiled chicken
35	1 slice Protegen toast	15	Watercress, radish, and cucumber salad	30	Asparagus spears
	Black coffee			45	½ cup yellow squash
1	Midmorning drink	43	D-Zerta butterscotch pudding	30	Endive salad with orange sections
		1	Midafternoon drink	50	Honeydew melon
					Black coffee
				58	6 oz. warm skim milk at bedtime

DEVILED EGG

1 hard-boiled egg per person   ½ tsp. Dijon mustard
1 tsp. Mayo 7   Pepper and salt

☞ Mash the yolk and mix well with other ingredients. Stuff egg whites and sprinkle with paprika.

TOTAL CALORIES FOR THE DAY: 565, INCLUDING 60 OF SNACKS

20	**Breakfast**	215	**Delicatessen Lunch**	270	**Dinner**
20	½ cup Mott's 5-Fruit Drink	100	2 oz. corned beef	160	4 oz. calves' liver
	Black coffee	100	1 oz. Swiss cheese	30	Green beans almondine*
1	Midmorning drink	15	Watercress and radishes	50	Spinach on a large artichoke bottom*
			Tea with lemon		
		1	Midafternoon drink	20	Mixed green salad
				10	Double orange dessert*
					Black coffee
				58	6 oz. skim milk at bedtime

We hope you saved some corned beef from the other day. Just remove all fat, serve it with good French mustard, and enjoy. Want a pickle? Have a big one.

Use the Teflon pan for the calves' liver and don't have it overdone.

GREEN BEANS ALMONDINE

☞ This should make you laugh. Take one large almond and shave it very thinly. Sprinkle over the top of the green beans.

SPINACH ON AN ARTICHOKE BOTTOM

☞ We discovered that you can buy canned artichoke bottoms packed in brine, very low in calories. Use frozen chopped spinach; season well, drain well, and pile in the artichoke bottom, which has been gently warmed.

DOUBLE ORANGE DESSERT

Serves 6.   Calories per serving: about 20.

☞ Dissolve contents of 2 envelopes of D-Zerta orange gelatin in 1 cup boiling water. Add 1½ cups low-calorie orange drink. Partially freeze. Beat 2 tablespoons ice water, 1 tablespoon lemon juice, and 2 tablespoons non-fat dry milk to stiff peaks. Beat frozen mixture until creamy. Fold in whipped milk. Return to freezer until partially frozen, stirring twice.

TOTAL CALORIES FOR THE DAY: 623, INCLUDING
60 OF SNACKS

	Breakfast		Lunch		Dinner
12	*Breakfast*	175	*Lunch*	376	*Dinner*
12	4 oz. cranberry juice Black coffee	125	Tomato stuffed with crab-meat*	290	Veal scalop-pini*
		50	½ grapefruit Tea with lemon	35	½ cup beets, julienne
1	Midmorning low-calorie drink			17	½ cup kale
		1	Midafternoon drink	34	Pear and cheese salad* Black coffee
				58	6 oz. skim milk at bedtime

TOMATO STUFFED WITH CRABMEAT

☞ Find a lovely large fresh tomato. Scoop out insides and drain well. Use the back-fin lump crabmeat. I know it's expensive, but think what you're saving not buying those hand-dipped chocolates! Mix the crabmeat with a little diet mayonnaise and lemon juice. Add a lot of chopped celery and stuff it into the tomato. Surround with fluffy greens and serve with a lemon wedge.

VEAL SCALOPPINI

Serves 3.   Calories per serving: 290.

2 Tbs. flour	1 Tbs. butter or margarine
¼ tsp. pepper	2 Tbs. sherry, or Marsala
½ tsp. salt	¼ cup beef broth
¾ lb. veal, cut for scaloppini	

☞ Mix together the flour, pepper, and salt and dip the veal in it. Then gently shake the veal so that most of the flour falls off. Melt the butter or margarine in the Teflon pan and brown the veal very quickly on both sides. Remove veal to a hot platter. Stir the sherry or Marsala into the pan, removing glaze; add the broth and cook quickly for 1 minute. Pour over the veal and serve.

PEAR AND CHEESE SALAD

Serves 2.   Calories per serving: about 34.

☞ Combine contents of 1 envelope of lime D-Zerta with ¼ teaspoon vinegar and a dash each of salt and ginger. Add 1 cup boiling water. Stir to dissolve. Chill until slightly thickened. Fold in 2½ tablespoons cottage cheese and ¼ cup drained diced dietetic pears. Chill until firm. Unmold on crisp greens.

TOTAL CALORIES FOR THE DAY: 680 (SKIP
THE MILK TODAY).

	Breakfast		*Lunch*		*Dinner*
50		145		485	
50	Slice of honey-dew with fresh lime	105	Oyster stew*	210	Rock Cornish game hen*
		20	2 Diet-10 crackers	140	Wild rice*
	Black coffee	20	Marinated green bean salad	45	Braised celery*
				15	Mixed green salad
			Tea with lemon	75	Fresh straw-berries
					Black coffee

Why don't you have some friends for dinner? This is a gala menu.

OYSTER STEW

6 medium oysters per person
5 oz. skim milk per person

White pepper
Salt
Pinch of thyme

☞ Pick the oysters over and heat in their own liquor until edges start to curl. Bring skim milk to boiling point and combine with oysters. Add seasonings.

ROCK CORNISH GAME HEN

Serves 6.   Calories per serving: 210.

2 tsp. salt
½ tsp. pepper

3 Rock Cornish game hens, 2½ lbs. each

2 Tbs. butter
½ cup dry white wine
2 Tbs. Madeira
¾ cup chicken broth

2 tsps. Kitchen Bouquet
½ cup seedless grapes, cut in
half (can be canned, but
use diet ones)

☞ Rub the salt and pepper into the hens. Melt the butter in a casserole. Place the hens in the casserole, breast side down. Roast in a 450-degree oven for 30 minutes, turning them breast up after the first 10 minutes. Reduce the heat to 350 degrees and roast 25 minutes longer, basting frequently with wine and broth. Remove hens and keep warm. Add the Madeira, and Kitchen Bouquet to the juice in the casserole. Cook over high heat until volume is reduced by half. Skim off any fat. Taste for seasoning. Add the grapes and cook 1 minute. Cut the hens in half and serve. If you have hungry gentlemen, you may serve them a whole hen. Ladies can't eat a whole one anyway, at least my little old lady couldn't even when she was in her heyday.

WILD RICE

Serves 6.   Calories per serving: 140.

1 cup wild rice
3 cups water
2 tsps. salt
2 Tbs. butter
1 onion, chopped fine

3 Tbs. chopped green pepper
½ lb. mushrooms, sliced
2 tsps. Worcestershire sauce
¼ tsp. freshly ground black
pepper

☞ Wash the rice in several changes of water. Put into pan and bring to a boil, adding salt. Remove cover, cook over medium heat for 30 minutes. Drain any remaining water. Melt the butter in a skillet; sauté the onion and green pepper 5 minutes. Add the mushrooms and sauté 5 minutes, stirring frequently. Combine with the rice, Worcestershire sauce, and pepper. Toss lightly and correct the seasoning.

[*continued*]

BRAISED CELERY

Serves 6.   Calories per serving: 45.

3 bunches celery	1 cup beef broth
2 Tbs. butter	½ tsp. Worcestershire sauce

☞ Remove the leaves and cut each celery bunch in quarters lengthwise. Melt the butter in the Teflon pan and sauté the celery until lightly browned. Add the broth and Worcestershire and cook over low heat 10 minutes, or until celery is tender but still crisp. Or you can use canned celery hearts for this. Cover with beef bouillon and heat in the oven until the bouillon is absorbed, about an hour.

TOTAL CALORIES FOR THE DAY: 609, INCLUDING 60 OF SNACKS

	Breakfast		*Lunch*		*Dinner*
55		195		299	
20	½ cup Mott's 5-Fruit Drink	100	Frankfurter	165	Chinese shrimp and peas*
35	1 slice Protegen bread Black coffee	30	Sauerkraut	100	½ cup cooked white rice
		20	Canned asparagus tips salad	25	Sliced tomato, onion, and cucumber salad
1	Midmorning drink	45	½ cup diet apricots Tea with lemon	9	Strawberry D-Zerta Black coffee
		1	Midafternoon drink	58	6 oz. warm skim milk at bedtime

CHINESE SHRIMP AND PEAS

Serves 3.   Calories per serving: 165.

1 Tbs. salad oil
¾ lb. shrimp, cleaned, shelled,
   deveined
3 scallions, chopped
1-inch piece of fresh ginger or
   1 tsp. powdered
1 clove garlic, mashed

1 cup Chinese snow pea pods
1 tsp. cornstarch
½ tsp. salt
Few drops of Sucaryl
1 tsp. soy sauce
¼ cup cold water

☞ Heat the oil in skillet or wok. Brown the shrimp lightly on both sides. Add the scallions, ginger, garlic, and peas. Cook over low heat for 2 minutes. Mix the cornstarch, salt, Sucaryl, soy sauce, and water and pour over the shrimp mixture. Stir constantly until it comes to a boil; simmer for 2 minutes. Taste for seasoning and serve with ½ cup white rice per person.

TOTAL CALORIES FOR THE DAY: 618, INCLUDING
60 OF SNACKS

70	*Breakfast*	128	*Lunch*	360	*Dinner*
70	1 soft-boiled egg Black coffee	50	2 Tbs. liver pâté* on	280	Chile con carne*
		28	2 slices Melba toast	20	½ cup brussels sprouts
1	Midmorning snack	50	½ grapefruit Tea with lemon	50	Waldorf salad
				10	Coffee jelly* Black coffee
		1	Midafternoon snack	58	6 oz. warm skim milk at bedtime

LIVER PÂTÉ

Calories per tablespoon: 25.

½ lb. chicken livers with sinews removed	¼ cup sherry ½ tsp. salt
1 slice onion	**Dash pepper**
¼ lb. raw mushrooms	

☞ Boil the chicken livers with the onion and mushrooms until soft. Place in blender with remaining ingredients and blend until smooth. Chill before serving. Put a speck of hard-boiled egg yolk that has been put through a sieve on top, and tuck a piece of parsley on the side.

CHILE CON CARNE

Serves 6.   Calories per serving: 280.

1 Tbs. salad oil	1 lb. round steak, ground
1 onion, chopped	1 1-lb. can kidney beans,
1 clove garlic, thinly chopped	drained
2 cups celery, sliced	2 1-lb. cans tomatoes
½ cup green pepper, chopped	Chili powder

☞ Heat the oil. Sauté garlic, onion, celery, and green pepper in a 4-quart kettle until onion is light brown. Add round steak and cook until it is well browned. Stir in kidney beans, tomatoes, and 1½ teaspoons chili powder. Simmer mixture over low heat for at least 45 minutes before serving. Just before serving, stir in enough more chili powder to give it the desired hotness. Makes 6 servings; remainder can be frozen.

COFFEE JELLY

Calories per serving: 10.

☞ Dissolve 1 tablespoon unflavored gelatin in ¼ cup cold water. Add 1¾ cups hot fresh coffee. Add 1 teaspoon liquid Sucaryl; mix well, pour into parfait glasses, and chill until firm.

TOTAL CALORIES FOR THE DAY: 559, INCLUDING 60 OF SNACKS

20	**Breakfast**	135	**Lunch**	344	**Dinner**
20	1 cup rhubarb* Black coffee	100	asparagus soufflé*	250	Boiled beef* with horse-radish
1	Midmorning drink	35	½ raw apple, sliced thin Tea with lemon	20	½ cup yellow turnip
				35	½ cup beets
		1	Midafternoon drink	9	Lime D-Zerta Black coffee
				58	6 oz. skim milk at bedtime

RHUBARB

☞ Do not use frozen rhubarb, unless it is the kind that comes in a bag with no sugar. Use Sucaryl to sweeten it. Hothouse rhubarb tastes wonderful. Don't overcook it.

ASPARAGUS SOUFFLÉ

Serves 2.   Calories per serving: 100.

6 cooked asparagus tips, chopped
1 tsp. flour
¼ cup skim milk

2 egg whites beaten to hold a peak
Salt and pepper
1 Tbs. butter

☞ Sprinkle asparagus with flour; add milk and fold in egg whites gently. Add salt and pepper. Pour mixture into buttered soufflé dish and bake in a preheated 375-degree oven until soufflé has risen and is delicately browned on top, about 20 minutes.

BOILED BEEF

Servings depend on the size of a piece of meat. ■ *Calories per serving (2 slices ½ inch thick): 250.*

2 whole cloves	2 carrots
1 onion	3 sprigs parsley
2 quarts water	1 bay leaf
4 lbs. first cut brisket of beef	3 peppercorns
2 stalks celery with leaves	1 Tbs. salt

☞ Stick the cloves into the onion. Bring the water to a boil in a deep pot; add the onion, beef, celery, carrots, parsley, bay leaf, and peppercorns. Skim. Bring to a boil again and add the salt. Cover and cook over low heat for 2½ hours, or until the meat is tender. Transfer the beef to a heated platter. Strain the stock, which can be used for bouillon.

TOTAL CALORIES FOR THE DAY: 615, INCLUDING
60 OF SNACKS

145	*Breakfast*	105	*Lunch*	305	*Dinner*
25	½ cup V-8 juice	50	½ cup skim-milk cottage cheese with	140	Clams casino*
				30	Stewed tomatoes
120	Scrambled egg on gluten toast	35	Chopped green onion, radishes, green pepper in a tomato cup	20	Spinach
	Black coffee			30	Jellied vegetable salad*
1	Midmorning drink	20	2 Diet-10 crackers	85	Profiteroles* with chocolate sauce
			Tea with lemon	58	6 oz. warm skim milk at bedtime
		1	Midafternoon drink		

Some days breakfast is much better than others. We tried to choose a day for a good one to go to the hairdresser. Or if you have to go to the bank and have to haggle with your trust officer. The days you are sitting around doing your jigsaw puzzle you can have one of the light ones.

CLAMS CASINO

Serves 3.   Calories per serving: 140.

18 cherrystone clams   3 slices half-cooked bacon,
2 Tbs. chopped green pepper   diced
2 Tbs. chopped pimento

☞ Have the fish man open the clams. Sprinkle some of the rest of the ingredients on each clam. Place in a baking dish or in 3 individual dishes (little copper ones are nice). Broil for 5 minutes. Serve immediately with lemon wedges.

JELLIED VEGETABLE SALAD

Serves 2.   Calories per serving: 30.

☞ Take 1 envelope of lemon D-Zerta. Dissolve in almost a cup of boiling water. Stir in 1 tablespoon vinegar. Chill until soupy. Meanwhile, back at the chopping block, mince scallions, carrots, green pepper, radishes, and a little cabbage. Stir in, pour in individual molds, and chill until firm. Serve on crisp greens with a couple of radishes alongside.

PROFITEROLES

☞ Stella d'Oro makes little creampuff things—dietetic. Very crisp and good. For each serving, split three puffs in half. Stuff each one with Borden's Dietetic Vanilla Ice Cream. On each puff put 1 teaspoon of Diet Delite chocolate sauce. Makes you feel as if you were OFF THIS AWFUL DIET.

TOTAL CALORIES FOR THE DAY: 612, INCLUDING
58 OF SNACKS

84	*Breakfast*	120	*Lunch*	350	*Dinner*
12	½ cup cranberry juice	60	½ can chicken noodle soup	30	Tomato madrilene with sherry*
50	½ cup Cream of Wheat	60	Whole orange Tea with lemon	190	Chicken in red wine*
22	2 oz. skim milk Black coffee		Have you tried "Constant Comment" tea? Nice for a change.	60	Asparagus with water chestnuts
	Midmorning drink (How about some of that beef bouillon from the boiled beef?) 0 calories			20	Cucumber and onion salad
				50	Chocolate pot de crème*
				58	6 oz. of warm skim milk at bedtime

TOMATO MADRILENE WITH SHERRY

Serves 3. Calories per serving: 30.

1 envelope plain gelatin	½ tsp. onion juice
1 cup tomato juice	2 Tbs. dry sherry
1 cup chicken stock	Salt and pepper to taste

☞ Soften the gelatin in ½ cup of the tomato juice. Combine the other ingredients and bring to a boil. Simmer a few minutes and stir in the softened gelatin. Pour into a shallow pan and chill until firm. Before serving, cut into cubes and pile in bouillon cups.

CHICKEN IN RED WINE

Serves 4.   Calories per serving: 190.

2 fryers, cleaned and quartered	½ cup red wine
¼ cup flour, seasoned with pepper and salt	¼ tsp. sage
	1 bay leaf
	Pinch of thyme
1 Tbs. cooking oil	¼ cup tomato juice
1 cup water	

☞ Shake the chicken with the seasoned flour in a paper bag. Heat the oil in an electric skillet to 400 degrees. Brown the chicken on all sides. Turn down to 200 degrees and add the water, wine, and other ingredients except the tomato juice. Cover and simmer for 1 hour. Remove the chicken to a warm platter. Add the tomato juice to the skillet. Stir and simmer for 5 minutes. Adjust the seasoning. Pour over the chicken before serving.

CHOCOLATE POT DE CRÈME

☞ Use D-Zerta chocolate pudding and serve in little chocolate pots with covers. Add a piece of lemon peel while cooking.

TOTAL CALORIES FOR THE DAY: 599, INCLUDING
58 OF SNACKS

50	*Breakfast*	196	*Lunch*	295	*Dinner*
50	½ cantaloupe with fresh lime	150	Split pea soup*	135	Finnan haddie*
		20	Mixed green salad	35	Green beans with mush-rooms
	Black coffee	26	Jellied prune whip (page 11)	25	½ cup carrots
	Midmorning			50	Hearts of palm salad*
	what have you		Tea with lemon		
			Midafternoon drink	50	½ grapefruit
					Black coffee
				58	6 oz. warm skim milk at bedtime

SPLIT PEA SOUP

Makes 6 cups.   Calories per cup: 150.

1 cup dried split peas	1½ cups soup stock (do you have any bouillon left?)
1 ham bone	
6 cups water	1 Tbs. potato flour
¼ cup onions, chopped	Salt and pepper, to taste
½ cup celery tops, chopped	Paprika
	¼ cup carrots, chopped

☞ Soak the dried split peas overnight in 3 cups of water. Drain and place the peas and ham bone in a soup kettle with 6 cups of water and simmer 3 hours. Then add the onions, celery, and carrots and simmer for another hour. Put the soup through the blender and add 1½ cups of soup stock. Allow to cool so that any fat will solidify on top and can be removed. To 1 tablespoon vegetable oil add 1 tablespoon potato flour. Add it slowly to the reheated—but not boiling—soup stock. Heat until the soup just comes to a boil. Taste for seasoning and add paprika, salt, and pepper to taste.

FINNAN HADDIE

Serves 3.   Calories per portion: 135. ■ *This is, in case you haven't run into it before, a smoked fish.*

¾ lb. finnan haddie filets	1 Tbs. butter or margarine
1 onion, sliced	1 Tbs. flour
1 cup skim milk	White pepper

☞ Wash the fish and soak for several hours in cold water. Drain and place the fish in a baking dish. Add the onion and milk. Bake in a 375-degree oven for 30 minutes. Drain; save the liquid. Make a sauce with the butter, flour, and reserved liquid; simmer for 5 minutes, until thickened. Season to taste with white pepper. This may be poured over the fish, or the fish may be flaked and mixed with the sauce.

HEARTS OF PALM SALAD

☞ Can't find a calorie count anywhere, so I guessed. We just put a lemony diet dressing and a few strips of pimento over the lovely white hearts.

TOTAL CALORIES FOR THE DAY: 603, INCLUDING
59 OF SNACKS

20	*Breakfast*	184	*Lunch*	340	*Dinner*
20	½ cup Mott's 5-Fruit Juice	175	Western omelet*	230	Roast leg of lamb*
	Black coffee	9	Raspberry D-Zerta	15	1 roasted onion
1	Midmorning snack		Tea with lemon	25	¼ cup green peas
			Midafternoon tea	20	Mixed green salad
				50	½ cup home-made apple-sauce
					Black coffee
				58	6 oz. warm skim milk at bedtime

WESTERN OMELET

☞ Get out your trusty Teflon pan. For two eggs, take 2
tablespoons chopped green pepper, 2 tablespoons chopped
onion, and 2 tablespoons chopped ham. Mix up with the eggs
and salt and pepper, pop into the pan, and make your omelet.

ROAST LEG OF LAMB

☞ Wipe lamb with damp cloth. Rub with cut piece of
garlic. Season well with salt, pepper, and MSG. Preheat oven to
450°. Place meat, fat side up on rack in roasting oven. Place
in oven. Reduce heat to 350°, and cook 30 minutes to a pound
for well done. On meat thermometer, 175° to 180°.

Roast onions round the meat; if you are having non-dieting guests, throw in a few potatoes for them. You may have 3 ounces of meat. Use your little scale to weigh it, and you'll be surprised how much you can have.

The applesauce is made without sugar; if it isn't sweet enough, add Sucaryl to taste. We like cinnamon on ours.

TOTAL CALORIES FOR THE DAY: 639, INCLUDING 58 OF SNACKS

12	*Breakfast*	273	*Lunch*	293	*Dinner*
12	½ cup cranberry juice	150	3 sardines* on lettuce leaves	165	Chicken livers Victor Hugo*
	Black coffee	80	Deviled egg (page 31)	25	Mustard greens
	Midmorning drink			20	Stewed celery
		43	½ cup fresh pineapple	20	Broccoli vinaigrette
			Tea with lemon	63	Mocha pot de crème*
			Midafternoon tea	58	6 oz. warm skim milk at bedtime

SARDINES

☞ Tenderly remove the sardines from their can and place them on paper towels. Pat them softly to remove as much oil as possible. Serve them with a generous squeeze of fresh lemon.

[*continued*]

CHICKEN LIVERS VICTOR HUGO

Serves 3.   Calories per serving: 165.

1 Tbs. butter	½ lb. mushrooms
1½ cloves garlic	¼ cup red wine
½ lb. chicken livers, halved	1½ tsps. cornstarch
½ tsp. salt	1 Tbs. water
Tiny pinch of ground cloves	Freshly ground black pepper
½ can consommé	

☞ In the top of a chafing dish or in an electric skillet, melt butter with garlic that has been put through a garlic press. Add chicken livers. Cook until no red juice runs from the livers. Add salt, cloves, consommé, and mushrooms, red wine. Cover and simmer for 10 minutes. Stir in the cornstarch mixed with water; cook 5 minutes longer, stirring constantly.

MOCHA POT DE CRÈME

Serves 3.   Calories per serving: 63.

¼ cup evaporated milk	1 square semi-sweet chocolate
5 oz. strong black coffee	(½ oz.)
1 envelope D-Zerta chocolate pudding	½ tsp. Sucaryl
	¾ tsp. brandy

☞ Combine evaporated milk and coffee in a saucepan. Stir in D-Zerta pudding. Add the chocolate and Sucaryl and stir over low heat until the chocolate is melted and a bare simmer is reached. Remove from the heat and add brandy. Pour into 3 little pots and chill.

TOTAL CALORIES FOR THE DAY: 664, INCLUDING
58 OF SNACKS

87	*Breakfast*	134	*Lunch*	385	*Dinner*
50	½ grapefruit	25	Tomato juice	250	Chili ham-burgers*
35	Protegen toast	100	Crabmeat salad with carrot sticks	30	Broiled tomato
2	Low-calorie jam			20	Zucchini
	Black coffee	9	Orange D-Zerta Tea with lemon	20	Salad with diet Roquefort dressing
	Midmorning drink		Midafternoon tea	65	Baked apple Black coffee
				58	6 oz. skim milk at bedtime

(Skip it if you can; we're 'way over today!)

Have a lovely lunch with that good crabmeat. Remember, get the really expensive kind, and ¾ cup is only a hundred calories.

CHILI HAMBURGERS

Serves 3.   Calories per serving: 250.

¾ lb. ground round steak	1 clove garlic, pressed
½ tsp. salt	1 scant tsp. chili powder
¼ tsp. pepper	½ cup water
1 small can of tomatoes, well drained	

☞ Mix the ground steak with the salt and pepper. Shape into skinny hamburgers. Heat Teflon pan and brown them well on both sides. Remove meat from skillet and add the remaining ingredients to the pan. Add ½ cup water and simmer sauce for 15 minutes. Pour over warm hamburgers.

TOTAL CALORIES FOR THE DAY: 643, INCLUDING
58 OF SNACKS

12	*Breakfast*	95	*Lunch*	478	*Dinner*
12	½ cup cranberry juice	0	Meat soup stock*	290	Curried lamb*
	Black coffee	50	Artichoke vinaigrette (page 18)	100	½ cup white rice
	Midmorning drink	45	Diet peaches	20	½ cup kohlrabi
			Tea with lemon	15	Mixed green salad
			Midafternoon drink	53	Baked pears Melba*
					Black coffee
				58	6 oz. warm skim milk at bedtime

MEAT SOUP STOCK WITH VEGETABLES

Makes 6 to 8 cups.   Calories when strained: o.

Flank of beef, 3½ lbs.
Giblets of 1 chicken
1 Tbs. salt
3 veal bones
½ cup onion, chopped
½ cup cabbage, chopped
1 leek

6 mushrooms
½ cup carrots, diced
½ cup celery with leaves, chopped
6 peppercorns
3 tomato skins

☞ Put the meat, giblets, salt, and bones into a large soup kettle. Cover with water and bring slowly to a boil. Skim. When boiling, add the other ingredients. Simmer covered for about 2 hours, or until meat is tender. Drain through a colan-

der. The meat can be served as boiled beef. Put the liquid
back on the stove and let simmer uncovered for about 1¼
hours, or until about 2 quarts of liquid remain. Strain through
cheesecloth. Cool and remove every speck of fat. Store in a
closed jar in the refrigerator, or freeze in amounts to serve
individually. Can also be used as a base for aspic or hot
bouillon. The same ingredients can be used to make chicken
soup—just substitute a whole chicken for the beef.

CURRIED LAMB

Serves 3 or 4. Calories per serving: 290. ■ *Use leftover
roast leg of lamb.*

☞ Use 3 ounces lamb per person. Remove all fat. Cut into
bite-size pieces. Brown 2 finely chopped onions in the Teflon
pan, which has been lightly rubbed with oil. Do not burn
them. Add a clove of garlic which has been put through a
garlic press, 1 bay leaf, ¼ teaspoon thyme, 1½ teaspoons curry
powder, 2 cups beef broth (from recipe above), and 1 teaspoon
of tomato paste. Mix 1 tablespoon cornstarch with 1 tablespoon
water and stir into the pan. When this is bubbling nicely and
has thickened a bit, add the pieces of lamb. Cook it just long
enough for the lamb to heat through. Add 1 tablespoon unsweetened coconut. Serve with rice.

BAKED PEARS MELBA

Serves 2. One half pear per person: 53 calories.

☞ Preheat oven to 350 degrees. Arrange pear halves in
baking dish. Pour ½ cup unsweetened pineapple juice, mixed
with ½ teaspoon Sucaryl and ¼ teaspoon ginger, over pears.
Bake, covered, for 45 minutes. Serve with 1 teaspoon red rasp-
berry dietetic preserves in each half pear.

TOTAL CALORIES FOR THE DAY: 645, INCLUDING
58 OF SNACKS

97	*Breakfast*	145	*Lunch*	345	*Dinner*
75	½ cup oatmeal	125	1 slice cold	225	Shad roe sauté*
22	2 oz. skim milk		boiled beef	50	Stuffed tomato
	Black coffee		with horse-		parisienne*
			radish	20	Fresh spinach
	Midmorning	20	Perfection		salad*
	drink		salad* on	50	Spanish melon
			greens		Black coffee
			Tea with lemon		
				58	6 oz. skim milk
			Midafternoon		at bedtime
			drink		

PERFECTION SALAD

☞ Use the classic recipe and leave out the sugar. Substitute Sucaryl.

SHAD ROE SAUTÉ

One half roe per serving. ■ *Calories per serving: 225.*

Shad roe	1 Tbs. parsley, chopped
1 onion	Crisp bacon, 1 slice per
1 tsp. salt	person
Trace of butter	

☞ Gently poach the roe in water with onion and salt in a deep skillet. Bring to a boil and simmer 15 minutes. Drain very carefully. Put a tiny piece of butter in your Teflon pan

and brown the roe lightly on both sides. Place on a hot platter
and garnish with parsley, bacon slices, and lemon wedges.

STUFFED TOMATO PARISIENNE

Serves 3.   Calories per serving: 50.

3 medium tomatoes	½ Tbs. parsley, chopped
½ Tbs. butter	1 oz. chicken broth, or enough
¼ lb. mushrooms, chopped	to cover the bottom of a
½ onion, chopped	baking dish
½ tsp. salt	
Dash pepper	

☞ Scoop out tomato pulp and save for another use. Sauté
the mushrooms and onions in the butter 5 minutes. Add salt,
pepper, and parsley, then stuff tomatoes. Cover bottom of
baking dish with chicken broth and arrange the tomatoes in it.
Bake in a 375-degree oven for 30 minutes.

FRESH SPINACH SALAD

☞ Choose very young, tender spinach. Wash it thoroughly
and dry. Chill for 1 hour in plastic wrap. Shred spinach into
bowl, cover with thinly sliced radishes, toss with low-calorie
Italian dressing.

TOTAL CALORIES FOR THE DAY: 564, INCLUDING
58 OF SNACKS

56	*Breakfast*	143	*Lunch*	307	*Dinner*
20	Mott's 5-Fruit Drink	100	Egg Florentine*	160	Calves' liver en brochette*
35	1 slice Protegen toast	43	½ cup diet pears	27	½ cup kale
1	low-calorie jam		Tea with lemon	45	½ cup winter squash
	Black coffee			20	Coleslaw
	Midmorning drink		Midafternoon tea	55	1 cup fresh strawberries
					Black coffee
				58	6 oz. skim milk at bedtime

EGG FLORENTINE

☞ *Florentine:* Whenever you see this, it means spinach. You can go out to lunch. Just cancel the Hollandaise sauce when you order this. You'll never miss it. Put a poached egg on top of ½ cup of nice fresh cooked spinach. Paprika, pepper, and salt.

There is probably some spinach left over from the salad last night, so cook it up, drain it well, put a poached egg on top. Sprinkle with paprika, salt, and pepper. *Voila!* Egg Florentine.

CALVES' LIVER EN BROCHETTE

4 oz. calves' liver per person: 160 calories. ■ *Here we go again with the skewers.*

☞ Cut the liver into 6 pieces. Alternate on a skewer with pieces of lemon. Broil for 3 or 4 minutes. Sprinkle with parsley, salt, and pepper and serve very hot.

The reason for all these strange leafy vegetables, like kale and turnip greens, is that they are so crammed full of vitamins. Put vinegar or lemon juice on them and it does help the taste. What I mean is, I know everybody doesn't like them. Not even me.

Incidentally, if you don't like your heavy meal at night, switch it to noon and have lunch at dinnertime.

TOTAL CALORIES FOR THE DAY: 534, INCLUDING
59 OF SNACKS

105	*Breakfast*	120	*Lunch*	250	*Dinner*
70	Poached egg on	55	½ can Camp-	145	Filet of sole
35	1 slice Protegen		bell's chicken		Veronique*
	bread		soup with	20	Broccoli
	Black coffee		rice	15	Mixed green
		20	2 Diet-10		salad
1	Midmorning		crackers	50	½ grapefruit
	snack	45	½ cup diet		drizzled with
			apricots		1 tsp. honey
			Tea with lemon		and heated
					under the
			Midafternoon		broiler
			tea		Black coffee
				58	6 oz. skim milk
					at bedtime

FILET OF SOLE VERONIQUE*

Serves 3.   Calories per serving: 145.

3 4-oz. filets of sole	1 Tbs. butter
1 tsp. salt	1 Tbs. flour
¼ tsp. white pepper	¾ cup skim milk
½ cup dry white wine	½ cup seedless white grapes
½ Tbs. lemon juice	(can be dietetic, canned)

☞ Season the fish with salt and pepper. Place in a lightly greased baking dish (not metal). Add the wine and lemon juice. Cover the dish. If it doesn't have a cover, use aluminum

* This means white grapes.

foil. Bake in a 350-degree oven for 15 minutes. Melt the butter in a saucepan. Blend in the flour, gradually add the milk. Stir constantly. Carefully remove the fish to a warm serving platter. Combine the juice left in the baking dish with the cream sauce. Add seasoning if needed. Pour over the filet, sprinkle the grapes around, and place the whole thing under the broiler to brown, which takes about 5 minutes.

TOTAL CALORIES FOR THE DAY: 617, INCLUDING 58 OF SNACKS

65	*Breakfast*	109	*Lunch*	385	*Dinner*
65	Whole orange, sliced	100	Jellied chicken loaf*	200	London broil*
	Black coffee	9	Orange D-Zerta	60	Stuffed mush-rooms*
	Midmorning bouillon		Tea with lemon	20	Italian green beans
			Midafternoon tea	30	Sliced tomato
				75	Angel cake*
					Black coffee
				58	6 oz. skim milk at bedtime

This could be somebody's birthday, even yours.

JELLIED CHICKEN LOAF

☞ Into 2 cups of chicken broth left from the Chicken in the Pot, dissolve 1 envelope of Knox unflavored gelatin. Add a little lemon juice. Chop celery, green pepper, and carrots—2

[*continued*]

tablespoons of each. When the gelatin has begun to thicken, stir in about ½ cup chicken cut in one-inch pieces, and vegetables cut small. Serves two. Pour into individual fancy molds and let set in the refrigerator. Serve on crisp chicory with a garnish of radishes and 2 small black olives per serving.

LONDON BROIL

Serves 6.   Calories per 3-ounce serving: 200.

4 Tbs. wine vinegar	1½ lbs. beef cut for London
1 tsp. salad oil	broil
½ tsp. garlic powder	

☞ Mix the vinegar, oil, and garlic powder. Marinate the meat in this mixture for several hours, turning it occasionally. Drain. Place the meat on a preheated broiler 2 inches below the heat: 4 minutes to a side for rare, 5 for medium, and 7 for well done. Cut diagonally, very thin. Very good cold, too.

STUFFED MUSHROOMS

Serves 1.   Calories per serving: 60.

4 good-sized mushrooms	Salt and pepper
1 tsp. butter	2 Tbs. cottage cheese
1 Tbs. onion, chopped	1 Tbs. dried breadcrumbs

☞ Remove mushroom stems, set caps aside for stuffing. Chop stems fine. Melt butter and sauté stems with chopped onion 5 minutes, stirring often. Add the salt and pepper, cottage cheese, and breadcrumbs. Mix well and stuff the mushrooms. Place them in Teflon pan and cook for 3 minutes over direct heat. Then broil for 3 minutes until brown.

ANGEL CAKE

Serves 16.   Calories per serving: 75.

1 cup sifted cake flour	1 tsp. cream of tartar
¾ cup sugar	½ tsp. vanilla
10 egg whites (1¼ cups)	1½ Tbs. Sucaryl
¼ tsp. salt	

☞ Preheat oven to 350 degrees. Sift the flour and 4 table-spoons of the sugar together. Beat the egg whites, salt, and cream of tartar together until thick and foamy. Add remaining sugar 2 tablespoons at a time, beating until stiff peaks form. Beat in vanilla and Sucaryl. Sift 2 tablespoons of the flour mixture at a time over egg whites and fold in gently after each addition. Turn into a 9-inch angel-cake pan. Bake 40 minutes, or until delicately browned and springy when pressed. Invert pan on a bottle and let cool, allowing the air to circulate around it. Run a spatula around the edge when cold and turn out of the pan. Happy birthday, dear Mama.

TOTAL CALORIES FOR THE DAY: 587, INCLUDING 60 OF SNACKS

12	*Breakfast*	245	*Lunch*	270	*Dinner*
12	½ cup cranberry juice	90	Shrimp curry*	25	Minestrone*
	Black coffee	100	½ cup cooked rice	120	Eggplant Parmigiana*
	Midmorning bouillon	20	Endive vinaigrette	25	Marinated green bean salad
		35	Snow pudding	100	Fruit and cheese plate*
			Midafternoon tea		Black coffee
				60	½ cup yogurt

SHRIMP CURRY

Serves 3.   Calories per serving: 90.

1 cup water	½ cup chopped onion
1 tsp. salt	1 Tbs. curry powder
1 bay leaf	¼ tsp. powdered ginger
1 stalk celery	¼ cup bouillon
¾ lb. shrimp	½ cucumber, diced
1½ Tbs. butter	1½ Tbs. lemon juice

☞ Combine the water, salt, bay leaf, and celery. Bring to a boil. Add the shrimp. Cook 5 minutes. Drain, reserving ½ cup of the shrimp stock. Peel shrimp. Melt butter in a saucepan, sauté the onion 5 minutes; stir in the curry powder, ginger, and bouillon. Cook over low heat 15 minutes. Add the shrimp, reserved stock, cucumber, and lemon juice. Cook 2 minutes. Serve with ½ cup rice per serving. Add 100 calories for the rice. Wow!

MINESTRONE

Serves 4.   Calories per serving: 25.

1 cup cold water
2 cups beef stock
½ cup shredded cabbage
1 stalk celery, diced
1 carrot, diced
1 tomato, peeled and diced
1 onion, peeled and sliced
  thin

1 sprig parsley
1 bay leaf
¼ tsp. savory
  Pinch thyme
  Salt and pepper to taste
  Grated Parmesan cheese

☞ Combine water and stock in soup pot. Add all the other ingredients except cheese and bring to a boil. Simmer over very low heat for ¾ hour or until vegetables are tender. Serve sprinkled with cheese.

EGGPLANT PARMIGIANA

Serves 3.   Calories per serving: 120.

1 small eggplant
½ Tbs. olive oil
¼ cup dry breadcrumbs
1½ Tbs. Parmesan cheese,
  grated
¼ tsp. salt

¼ tsp. pepper
¼ tsp. garlic powder
½ cup canned tomato sauce
3 thin slices Mozzarella
  cheese

☞ Peel the eggplant and slice ¼ inch thick. Pour boiling water over the slices and let them soak 5 minutes. Drain and dry. Heat the oil in the Teflon pan; brown eggplant on both sides. Mix together the breadcrumbs, cheese, salt, pepper, and garlic powder. In a baking dish arrange layers of eggplant, breadcrumb mixture, and tomato sauce. Cover with Mozzarella. Bake in a 325-degree oven for 25 minutes.

FRUIT AND CHEESE PLATE

Cheese is very full of calories, so concentrate on the fruit. Pears and apples sliced very thin with a few grapes. Looks lovely.

TOTAL CALORIES FOR THE DAY: 641, INCLUDING
58 OF SNACKS

122	*Breakfast*	150	*Lunch*	311	*Dinner*
50	1 slice Spanish melon	100	Clam chowder*	160	4 thin slices beef tongue*
50	½ cup Cream of Wheat	50	½ grapefruit Tea with lemon	21	½ cup turnip greens
22	2 oz. skim milk Black coffee		Midafternoon tea	35	½ cup beets
				20	Hearts of lettuce with diet Russian dressing
	Midmorning diet drink			75	1 baked apple Black coffee
				58	6 oz. skim milk at bedtime

CLAM CHOWDER

Serves 2.   Calories per serving: 100.

1 tsp. butter	White pepper
1 onion	¼ tsp. celery salt
1 Tbs. flour	1 small potato, diced
1 cup water	½ cup skim milk
1 tsp. salt	1 can minced clams

☞ Melt the butter and sauté the onion for 10 minutes, until soft, stirring frequently. Sprinkle the flour on top of the onion; pour in any liquid from the clams; add the water, salt, pepper, celery salt, and potato. Cover and cook over low heat 10 minutes. Add the milk and the clams and bring slowly to the boiling point, but do not boil. Serve at once.

BEEF TONGUE

beef tongue	10 peppercorns
1 onion	celery tops
1 carrot	

☞ If the tongue is smoked, simmer in water to cover for 10 minutes. Drain—put in seasoned water, peppercorns, sliced onion, carrot, celery tops, and simmer uncovered for 2 or 3 hours, until tender. If the tongue is to be served hot, remove from water, plunge into ice water to cool enough for handling. Remove skin, and roots and gristle. Trim nicely. Return to pot to keep warm. Slice diagonally, near tip, to make attractive slices.

TOTAL CALORIES FOR THE DAY: 621, INCLUDING
58 OF SNACKS

50 *Breakfast*	173 *Lunch*	340 *Dinner*
50 ½ grapefruit Black coffee Midmorning beef bouillon	110 Fruit Salad ¼ cup cottage cheese in ½ medium cantaloupe garnished with grapes and straw- berries 63 D-Zerta Butter- scotch pudding Tea with lemon	250 Stuffed Beef Roast * 15 ½ cup cauli- flower 20 1 cup celery, stewed 15 Mixed green salad 40 ½ cup diced fresh pine- apple 58 6 oz. skim milk at bedtime

STUFFED BEEF ROAST

Serves 6 or more. Calories per 3 oz. serving: 250. ▪ *This is also great cold. And if you have a large piece left put it in the freezer.*

Rolled Roast of Beef, around 5 or 6 pounds 1 piece of Pepperoni	(dried Italian sausages) Salt and freshly ground black pepper

☞ Take a long skinny knife and push it lengthwise through the center of the meat. Insert the pepperoni in this hole, pushing it firmly in, but don't let it protrude from the other end. Sprinkle the meat with salt and freshly ground black pepper and place it in a roasting pan. Cook it at 325 degrees for 30 minutes per pound, for medium, less for rare. Let stand for 20 minutes after removing from the oven to make slicing easier.

TOTAL CALORIES FOR THE DAY: 577, INCLUDING
58 OF SNACKS

20	*Breakfast*	140	*Lunch*	359	*Dinner*
20	Mott's 5-Fruit	10	Beef bouillon	275	4 oz. pot roast*
	Drink	130	Chef's salad*	40	2 carrots
	Black coffee		Tea with lemon	35	1 onion
				9	Raspberry
	Midmorning				D-Zerta
	diet drink				Black coffee
				58	6 oz. warm skim
					milk at
					bedtime

CHEF'S SALAD

Serves 1. Calories per serving: 130.

☞ Lots of fresh crisp greens with 3 thin slices tongue cut in julienne and ½ ounce Swiss cheese, also julienne. Arrange on top of the greens and serve with any diet French, Russian, or Roquefort dressing.

POT ROAST

4 oz. meat: 275 calories.

3 lbs. beef, eye round	½ tsp. garlic powder
2 onions, chopped	1 cup beef broth, fresh or
2 tsps. salt	canned
½ tsp. salt	Canned onions
¼ tsp. pepper	Canned carrots
1 bay leaf	

[*continued*]

☞ Heat a Dutch oven, rub lightly with a piece of suet, brown the meat well on all sides. Do not burn. Add the onions and brown them. Sprinkle with the other ingredients and add broth (sometimes we put in some red wine). Cover and cook over low heat for 2½ hours, or until tender. Remove from heat, strain off gravy, and put in the freezer for the fat to congeal. Remove every speck of fat; taste for seasoning. Reheat the gravy and put the beef back in to get hot. Put the carrots and onions in at the same time, to warm through.

TOTAL CALORIES FOR THE DAY: 602, INCLUDING 58 OF SNACKS

48	*Breakfast*	156	*Lunch*	340	*Dinner*
12	Cranberry juice	126	Vegetable plate salad*	200	Cabbage rolls*
35	½ slice Protegen toast with	30	1 fresh plum	80	½ cup mashed potato
1	Low-calorie jam		Tea with lemon	60	Rum-baked pears*
	Black coffee		Midafternoon		Black coffee
	Midmorning drink		tea	58	6 oz. skim milk at bedtime

VEGETABLE PLATE SALAD

This can be outstanding if you are feeding a group. If you're not feeding a group, you can use up all the leftover dibs and dabs of vegetables in the refrigerator.

	AMOUNT PER SERVING
Cauliflower	½ cup: 15 cal.
Peas	¼ cup: 27 cal.
Carrots	1 medium: 20 cal.
Yellow squash	½ cup: 15 cal.
Broccoli	½ cup: 20 cal.
Green beans	½ cup: 12 cal.
Beets	½ cup: 17 cal.

☞ Put the cauliflower in the middle. These are all cooked vegetables, by the way, and if you prefer them warm, you may have it that way. Or chilled with a little diet salad dressing. The picture you make with all the lovely bright colors will be most pleasing.

CABBAGE ROLLS

2 cabbage rolls per serving: 200 calories. ■ *A wonderful old Hungarian sitter we had for our first set of children taught me to make these.*

1 large head cabbage	1 lb. very lean ground beef
3 onions	2 tsps. salt
1 #2½ can tomatoes	¼ cup raw rice
Veal knuckle or piece of bacon rind	1 beaten egg
1 #2½ can sauerkraut	2 tsps. cold water
1 onion, grated	6 peppercorns

☞ Cover the cabbage with boiling water and let sit until cool enough to handle. You want to separate 12 large leaves.

[continued]

Slice the onions and place in a pot with the tomatoes, bones or bacon rind, and sauerkraut. Grate another onion and mix with the beef, salt, rice, egg, and water. Mix well. Place a heaping tablespoon of this on each cabbage leaf. Nature designed these for rolling. They just go together so easily. If they don't, use a toothpick to hold them together. Carefully arrange the cabbage rolls in their nest of sauerkraut, add the peppercorns, cover and cook over low heat for 1½ hours. Be sure they don't cook dry. If there is any fat visible, skim it off.

RUM-BAKED PEARS

Serves 4.   Calories per serving: 60.

8 pear halves, canned, dietetic	2 Tbs. rum
1 Tbs. Sucaryl	3 Tbs. water

☞ Combine Sucaryl, rum, and water. Arrange pears in baking dish. Spoon liquid into each pear half. Bake in 350-degree oven for 30 minutes.

TOTAL CALORIES FOR THE DAY: 600, INCLUDING
58 OF SNACKS

85	*Breakfast*	150	*Lunch*	307	*Dinner*
50	½ cup orange juice	150	Chinese pepper steak*	180	Chicken Marengo*
35	Protegen toast with cinnamon		Tea with lemon	20	Beet greens
				12	Wax beans
	Black coffee		Midafternoon drink	15	Salad
				50	Strawberries Romanoff*
	Midmorning drink				Black coffee
				58	6 oz. skim milk at bedtime

CHINESE PEPPER STEAK

☞ Use either leftover pot roast or London broil. Take 2 ounces of cooked meat sliced very thin and 1 green pepper, cut in 1-inch square pieces. Slice 2 stalks of celery diagonally. Make a gravy of 1 cup beef bouillon thickened with 1 teaspoon cornstarch mixed with 1 teaspoon cold water. Add 1 tablespoon soy sauce. Slice 1 onion vertically and cook all this in your wok or skillet to 6 or 8 minutes.   [*continued*]

CHICKEN MARENGO

Serves 3.   Calories per serving: 180.

1½ Tbs. flour	¼ tsp. thyme
1 tsp. salt	1 tomato, peeled and diced
¼ tsp. pepper	½ cup dry white wine
1 2-lb. chicken, cut up	¼ cup mushrooms, quartered
½ Tbs. olive oil	1 Tbs. parsley, chopped
1 stalk celery	1 Tbs. cognac
1 sprig parsley	1 clove garlic, pressed
1 bay leaf	

☞ Mix the flour, salt, and pepper and put it in a paper bag with the chicken. Shake well. Heat the olive oil in the Teflon pan and brown the chicken. Transfer chicken to a casserole; warm the cognac, pour it over the chicken, and set aflame. When the flame goes out, add garlic, celery, parsley, bay leaf, thyme, tomatoes, and wine. Cover and cook over low heat 30 minutes. Add the mushrooms and cook 15 minutes longer, or until the chicken is tender. Taste for seasoning. Remove the celery, parsley, and bay leaf. Sprinkle with the chopped parsley and serve from the casserole.

STRAWBERRIES ROMANOFF

Serves 3.   Calories per serving: 80.

1½ cups fresh strawberries	¼ tsp. Sucaryl
¼ cup orange juice	¾ cup low-calorie whipped
1 oz. Grand Marnier	cream*

☞ Combine the orange juice, Sucaryl, and Grand Marnier and pour over the strawberries in your best Steuben crystal bowl. Marinate for at least 1 hour. Refrigerate until needed. At serving time, place matching bowl of whipped cream on a tray and serve together, or toss them up in the kitchen and place in one bowl, though this is not nearly so spectacular.

LOW-CALORIE WHIPPED CREAM

Makes 1 cup. Calories per tablespoon: 4.

¼ cup evaporated skim milk, chilled in freezer for a few hours

¾ tsp. unflavored gelatin, softened in 1 tsp. water

¼ cup boiling water

1½ tsps. Sucaryl

1½ tsps. vanilla

½ tsp. lemon juice

☞ Pour ¼ cup evaporated milk into refrigerator tray and chill until ice crystals begin to form around the edge. Chill a mixing bowl and rotary beaters. Soak gelatin in cold water for about 5 minutes. Pour boiling water over and stir until gelatin is dissolved. Meanwhile, spoon chilled evaporated milk from tray into chilled mixing bowl. Add Sucaryl and flavoring. Beat rapidly for about 10 minutes, until thick and creamy. Add thickened gelatin mixture and lemon juice and continue beating until good whipped-cream consistency is obtained. This whipped-cream topping can be served immediately, but for even better results refrigerate in the freezer compartment for at least 1 hour. Beat again immediately before serving.

If this is all too much trouble, rush down to your friendly neighborhood grocer and buy Cremora or Lucky Whip or one of those. Just be sure it is low in calories.

TOTAL CALORIES FOR THE DAY: 660, INCLUDING
58 OF SNACKS

130	*Breakfast*	240	*Lunch*	232	*Dinner*
80	Scrambled egg	160	Stuffed lobster	150	Sweetbreads in
50	1 slice crisp		tail*		wine*
	bacon	35	Tomato au	12	½ cup green
	Black coffee		gratin*		beans
		45	½ cup diet	20	Braised leeks*
	Midmorning		peaches	15	Mixed green
	drink		Tea with lemon		salad
				35	1 medium
			Midafternoon		tangerine
			drink		Black coffee
				58	6 oz. skim milk
					at bedtime

STUFFED LOBSTER TAIL

Serves 4.   Calories per serving: 160.

4	cooked lobster tails	1	small can diet cream of
1	Tbs. oil		mushroom soup
1	medium onion, minced	1	tsp. Worcestershire sauce
1	small can sliced mushrooms,	½	cup dry white wine
	drained		Salt and pepper
			Paprika

☞ Heat the oil in a skillet and sauté the onion for 10 minutes, stirring frequently. Add the mushrooms and cook 3 more
minutes. Stir in the mushroom soup, Worcestershire sauce, and
wine. Taste for seasoning. Simmer for several more minutes,
stirring constantly. Remove the lobster meat from the shells,

saving the shells. Cut the meat in small pieces and add to the sauce. Heat through. Refill the shells and sprinkle with paprika.

TOMATO AU GRATIN

☞ Slice the top off 1 tomato per person. Sprinkle with Parmesan cheese and bake in a moderate oven until the tomato is soft but still holds its shape.

SWEETBREADS IN WINE

Serves 2.   Calories per serving: 150.

1 pair sweetbreads	¼ tsp. pepper
1 cup water	⅛ tsp. thyme
½ tsp. vinegar	¼ cup sweet sherry
½ tsp. salt	1 Tbs. butter
½ onion, chopped	

☞ Wash the sweetbreads and soak in cold water for 20 minutes. Drain, place in pot, and cover with 1 cup water, vinegar, and ¼ teaspoon salt. Bring to a boil. Cover and cook over low heat for 15 minutes. Let cool in liquid 15 minutes. Drain. Remove the membranes and cube the sweetbreads. Melt the butter in a skillet; sauté the onion and sweetbreads 5 minutes. Add the pepper, thyme, sherry, and remaining salt. Cook over low heat 5 minutes. Serve garnished with parsley and lemon.

BRAISED LEEKS

☞ Use 2 whole leeks per person. Cover with fat-free chicken broth and cook for 40 minutes in a 350-degree oven, or until leeks are tender.

TOTAL CALORIES FOR THE DAY: 514, INCLUDING
58 OF SNACKS

12	*Breakfast*	119	*Lunch*	325	*Dinner*
12	Cranberry juice	80	2 slices cold	230	Crabmeat
	Black coffee		tongue with		Creole*
			mustard	20	Asparagus
	Midmorning	30	Sliced tomato	25	Stuffed celery*
	bouillon		with oregano,	50	Melon with
			black pepper,		fresh lime
			and vinegar		Black coffee
		9	Lime D-Zerta		
			Tea with lemon	58	6 oz. warm skim
					milk at
			Midafternoon		bedtime
			tea		

CRABMEAT CREOLE

Serves 3.   Calories per serving: 230.

1 Tbs. butter or margarine	¾ lb. crabmeat
2 onions, finely chopped	8 green olives, chopped
1 Tbs. flour	2 tsps. Worcestershire sauce
¾ cup chicken broth	¼ tsp. freshly ground black
1 cup canned tomatoes,	pepper
drained	1 tsp. salad oil
1 green pepper, chopped	2 Tbs. breadcrumbs
¼ tsp. dried thyme	2 Tbs. parsley, chopped

☞ Melt the butter in a saucepan. Sauté the onions for 5
minutes. Blend in the flour; gradually add the broth, stirring
constantly to the boiling point. Add the tomatoes, green pepper, parsley, and thyme. Simmer for 15 minutes. Stir in the

crabmeat, olives, Worcestershire sauce, and pepper. Taste for seasoning. Grease a 1½-quart casserole with the oil and dust with crumbs. Turn the crabmeat mixture into it. Bake in a 375-degree oven for 15 minutes. Serve from the casserole. This is a good one to get ready in the morning. All you have to do at dinnertime is slide it in the oven.

STUFFED CELERY

Serves 1.   Calories per serving: 25. ■ *Take 2 stalks of celery, trim nicely, and stuff with the following:*

2 Tbs. cottage cheese Dash of tabasco
1 tsp. Worcestershire sauce Sprinkle of paprika
1 Tbs. diet Roquefort dressing

The stuffed stalks can be cut into bite-size pieces.

TOTAL CALORIES FOR THE DAY: 607, INCLUDING
58 OF SNACKS

55	*Breakfast*	85	*Lunch*	409	*Dinner*
20	½ cup Mott's 5-Fruit Drink	40	Onion soup*	285	Swedish meatballs*
35	1 slice Protegen toast with low-calorie jam	15	Mixed green salad	85	Noodle ring*
	Black coffee	30	Vanilla pudding Tea with lemon	12	½ cup green beans
	Midmorning drink		Afternoon tea	15	Watercress and cucumber salad
				12	Pink Zip* Black coffee

58 (If you are tired of warm milk at bedtime, try a small orange or a small apple or some seedless grapes. Just don't go to bed hungry.)

ONION SOUP

Serves 3.   Calories per serving: 40.

2 large onions, peeled and sliced thin	3 cups beef broth ⅛ cup Worcestershire sauce

☞ Place all the ingredients in a pot and simmer, covered, for 30 minutes. If you must have cheese, remember that 1 tablespoon of grated Parmesan will cost you 28 calories.

SWEDISH MEATBALLS

Serves 6.   Calories per serving: 285. ■ *Can be frozen.*

1 slice bread, crumbled	1 tsp. salt
¼ cup skim milk	¼ tsp. pepper
1 Tbs. butter	⅛ tsp. nutmeg
4 Tbs. onion, finely chopped	¼ cup dry white wine
1 lb. ground lean beef	3 Tbs. half-and-half sour
1 egg, beaten	cream
3 Tbs. ice water	1 Tbs. chopped parsley

☞ Soak the bread in the milk. Melt butter in a skillet and sauté the onion for 5 minutes. Combine the soaked bread, onions, meat, egg, water, salt, pepper, and nutmeg. Shape into balls about the size of a walnut. (If you dip your hands in cold water, the meat doesn't stick.) In the same skillet you sautéed the onion in, brown the meatballs on all sides. Transfer to a hot platter. Pour the wine into the skillet, stir well; then, stirring vigorously, add the sour cream, 1 tablespoon at a time. When well blended, pour over the meatballs and place them in the middle of the noodle ring. Sprinkle with chopped parsley.

NOODLE RING

Serves 6.   Calories per serving: 85.

½ lb. medium-fine noodles	¼ tsp. freshly ground black
2 egg yolks	pepper
½ cup skim milk	½ tsp. paprika
2 tsp. melted butter	2 egg whites, stiffly beaten
1 tsp. salt	

☞ Cook the noodles in boiling salted water 2 minutes less than it says on the package. Drain and rinse with cold water.

[*continued*]

Beat together the egg yolks, milk, butter, salt, pepper, and paprika. Stir in the noodles and fold in the egg whites. Turn into a lightly greased 8-inch ring mold. Set in a shallow pan of water. Bake 40 minutes in a 350-degree oven.

PINK ZIP

Serves 4.   Calories per serving: 12.

☞ Dissolve contents of 1 envelope of D-Zerta strawberry gelatin and 1 envelope of D-Zerta lemon gelatin in 1 cup boiling water. Chill until syrupy. Stir in 1 cup low-calorie ginger ale. Pour into sherbet glasses and chill until firm.

TOTAL CALORIES FOR THE DAY: 610, INCLUDING 58 OF SNACKS

67	*Breakfast*	135	*Lunch*	350	*Dinner*
45	½ cup cornflakes	80	Curried deviled egg (2 halves)*	210	Scampi*
22	2 oz. skim milk			50	Eggplant Provençal*
	Black coffee	5	Dill pickle, watercress, radishes	25	Cauliflower
	Midmorning drink			15	Mixed green salad
		50	½ grapefruit Tea with lemon	40	Lemon sherbet*
					Black coffee
			Midafternoon tea	58	6 oz. warm skim milk at bedtime

CURRIED DEVILED EGG

4 hard-boiled eggs	Pepper and salt
1 tsp. prepared mustard	Paprika
1 tsp. Worcestershire sauce	
Pinch of curry powder, to taste	

☞ Mix all ingredients together until you have a smooth paste. Pipe into the whites (or pile in with a spoon) and sprinkle with paprika. Put a parsley sprig on each half.

SCAMPI

Serves 3 or 4. Eight shrimp per serving: 210 calories.

☞ There are as many recipes to cook scampi as there are Italian restaurants in New York City, most of them good. Peel your shrimp. Leaves the tails on. Make a marinade of diet Italian dressing thinned with fresh lemon juice and with several cloves of garlic pressed into it, lots of freshly ground black pepper, and ½ green pepper minced fine. Marinate the shrimp for several hours, turning frequently. Place on broiler, about 3 inches from heat, and broil 3 minutes on each side. Serve with lemon wedges.

EGGPLANT PROVENÇAL

Serves 2. Calories per serving: 50.

2 eggplants, peeled and chopped	Pinch dried tarragon
3 large tomatoes, chopped	2 green olives, chopped
Juice of 1 lemon	Salt and pepper

[continued]

☞ Put the eggplants and the tomatoes into a small saucepan. Add the lemon juice, tarragon, olives, and the salt and pepper. Simmer over very low heat for ½ hour with pan tightly covered.

LEMON SHERBET

Serves 8. Calories per serving: 40. Just keep the rest in your freezer.

1½ cups water	¼ cup powdered skim milk
2 tsps. Sucaryl	Few drops of yellow food
½ cup lemon juice	coloring, if desired
½ cup orange juice	8 tsps. creme de menthe
1 tsp. lemon rind	

☞ Combine water, Sucaryl, lemon juice, orange juice, and lemon rind. Heat. Cool and strain. Add the dry milk and food coloring and mix well. Place in freezer tray for 45 minutes. Turn into chilled bowl and beat with electric beater until frothy. Return to freezer until almost set. Beat again with chilled bowl and beaters and freeze again until firm enough to spoon out. Top with 1 teaspoon of creme de menthe per serving.

SPRING MENUS

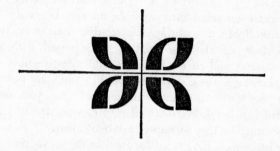

Spring is the season of simplicity. The taste of the tiny new foods should not be hidden, for the delicacy of their flavors must be savored. These very facts are the greatest help to the dieter. Nothing tastes as delicious as the very first asparagus, cooked to crisp perfection and served with just a squeeze of fresh lemon juice. This usually happens about the same time that the BONED SHAD sign appears in the fish-market window. Bibb lettuce is on hand, too. Add fresh strawberries for dessert, and there is a menu you could use to entertain the Queen, or Julia Child, or James Beard.

Cranshaw melons come in now from California, plums from South America, grapes—the little green seedless ones—limes and lemons and nectarines are ready for your table. Fresh spinach, to serve *en branche,* or the tiny new leaves mixed with radishes and bacon, make a very different salad. Zucchini stuffed with tomatoes will have your family (not you, though) asking for seconds. Have a tiny baby lamb for Easter instead of ham. Greek or Italian markets can usually obtain this for you if given advance notice, or roast a leg of lamb. Long Island duckling, famed the world over, is permitted the dieter if it is cooked on a rotisserie. All the fat drips off, and there is left the delicious dark meat of the duckling. Your dieter's portion may be small, but the taste is divine.

With winter past, the lobstermen set forth again to set their traps. A one-pound lobster has only about 100 calories. Think how long it takes to eat and savor a lobster; discover the flavor by squeezing on a little lemon juice. Shrimp is abundant for salad or for lightly curried scampi. A cold *gazpacho* can be served and even salad-haters gobble up this heavenly "salad soup" from Spain. Borscht is a way to disguise the lowly beet. Lamb kebabs on skewers, brightly interspersed with green-pepper squares and cherry tomatoes, add a festive note to the dieter's day. Eggs, the old-time symbol of spring, are now available all year long. An omelet, made in a Teflon pan, makes a delightful luncheon. Hard-boiled eggs can be stuffed with almost anything—a tiny shrimp or a dab of caviar.

Baby is the definitive word for food in the springtime: Baby peas, baby lamb, tiny baby apricots from California; the very first baby radishes from your garden. (You can eat all the radishes you want—forty or fifty if you can hold them. I informed my little old lady of this fact, but I will not tell you what she replied. However, *I* happen to *like* radishes.)

There are many foods the dieter must avoid, or should take only in minute quantities, but the salads and vegetables that appear in the spring can be savored in fairly large amounts, provided a low-calorie dressing is used. If you are starting your diet in the spring (was it the fitting-room blues?) remember to start your marketing at the fresh produce part of the shop or supermarket. Skip the ice cream and the baked goods, but concentrate on fish and the beautiful fresh fruit and vegetables that are now so easily found in most American markets.

Spring Menus

Main dishes for dinner

❧ WEEK 1 ❧

Filet of sole
Rotisserie chicken
Deviled roast beef
Tripe à la mode de Caen
Fish paprikas
Broiled lamb chop
Lamb stew

❧ WEEK 2 ❧

Broiled hamburger
Calves' liver
Crabmeat à la Palace
Veal chop casserole
Chicken chow mein
Filet of sole Almondine
Sauerbraten

❧ WEEK 3 ❧

Veal Marsala
Barbecued spareribs

Stuffed lobster tails
Lamb shanks Drennan
Sirloin steak
Cioppino
Chicken Hawaiian

⟬ WEEK 4 ⟭

Pickled walnut stew
Filet of flounder Portuguese
Minute steak Diane
Crown roast of lamb
Oysters Rockefeller
Salmon divan
Veal paprika

⟬ WEEK 5 ⟭

Short ribs Kikkoman
Mussels
Sukiyaki
Frankfurter Hungarian
Corned beef and cabbage
Roast turkey
Deviled crabmeat

⟬ WEEK 6 ⟭

Turkey divan
Spring stew
Herb-broiled chicken
Bouillabaisse
Tournedos de boeuf
Coquilles St. Jacques
Ham soufflé

TOTAL CALORIES FOR THE DAY: 619, INCLUDING
60 OF SNACKS

70	*Breakfast*	325	*Lunch*	164	*Dinner*
27	½ cup fresh strawberries	20	Clear chicken broth	90	4 oz. filet of sole, broiled with low-calorie salad dressing
43	1 slice gluten toast with low-calorie jam Black coffee	150	1 frankfurter on		
		155	Roll, with mustard, pickle Tea with lemon	25	Stewed tomatoes
1	Midmorning snack (try some of that vegetable broth)	1	Midafternoon goodie	25	Green beans
				15	Small salad
				9	Lemon D-Zerta Black coffee
				58	6 oz. warm skim milk at bedtime

Nothing complicated to cook today. You could even go to the ball game, if there is one, and have your lunch there. The first strawberries are in the market and they taste wonderful! The frankfurter will be better if you heat the bun. If you like relish, go ahead. The sole will look better if you put some paprika on it and serve it with lemon. (Have you noticed how hooked I am on lemon? It makes everything taste fresher. I even put it in my chicken broth.)

TOTAL CALORIES FOR THE DAY: 597, INCLUDING
58 OF SNACKS

67 *Breakfast*	138 *Lunch*	334 *Dinner*
45 ½ cup oatmeal	9 Bouillon	224 Rotisserie
22 2 oz. skim milk	20 2 Diet-10	chicken*
Black coffee	crackers	37 ¼ cup baby
	50 ¼ cup cottage	limas
Midmorning	cheese with	20 ½ cup green
drink	50 Fresh fruit	beans
	9 Orange D-Zerta	15 Cucumber and
	Tea with lemon	red onion
		salad
	Midafternoon	38 ½ cup diet
	drink	peaches
		Black coffee
		58 6 oz. skim milk
		at bedtime

ROTISSERIE CHICKEN

Calories per 4-ounce serving: 224.

☞ Take 1 small whole chicken, ready to cook. Sprinkle heavily inside and out with Lowry's Seasoned Salt and truss up to put on the rotisserie. Follow the manufacturer's directions, but cook until it is crisp and golden brown and delicious. The fat cooks out and all you have left is something wonderful. It's good cold. If anybody wants you to go on a picnic, and if they are fried chicken-type people, this is a good thing to take. It tastes better—not soggy.

TOTAL CALORIES FOR THE DAY: 592, INCLUDING
58 OF SNACKS

76	*Breakfast*	140	*Lunch*	318	*Dinner*
40	½ cantaloupe	55	½ can Camp-	240	Deviled roast
35	1 slice Protegen		bell's chicken		beef*
	toast with		soup with	12	½ cup wax
1	Low-calorie jam		rice		beans
		40	4 artichoke	25	Grilled tomato
	Midmorning		hearts on	15	Salad
	drink		watercress	26	Grapefruit
		45	D-Zerta choco-		strawberry
			late pudding		delight*
			Tea with lemon		Black coffee
			Midafternoon	58	6 oz. skim milk
			tea		at bedtime

DEVILED ROAST BEEF

☞ If your roast beef was a standing (rib) one, take 1 bone
per person. If it was a boneless roast, take two slices per person.
Remove all visible fat. Sprinkle with vinegar and Worcestershire sauce. Spread with Dijon mustard and sprinkle lightly
with fine dry breadcrumbs. Place under broiler until bubbly.

GRAPEFRUIT STRAWBERRY DELIGHT

Serves 2.   Calories per serving: about 26.

☞ Dissolve contents of 1 envelope of D-Zerta strawberry
gelatin in 1 cup boiling water. Chill until slightly thickened.
Fold in 6 sections unsweetened grapefruit. Chill in molds.

TOTAL CALORIES FOR THE DAY: 623, INCLUDING 58 OF SNACKS

70	*Breakfast*	75	*Lunch*	420	*Dinner*
70	Soft-boiled egg Black coffee	75	Tomato stuffed with crabmeat	285	Tripe à la mode de Caen*
	Midmorning drink		Tea with lemon	20	Carrots
			Midafternoon tea	20	Cold broccoli vinaigrette
				115	Apple Betty* Black coffee
				58	6 oz. skim milk at bedtime

TRIPE À LA MODE DE CAEN

Serves 6. Calories per serving: 285. ■ *This is unbelievably good. Takes forever to cook. Do it the night before; cook overnight and take it off at breakfast and reheat it for dinner.*

2 lbs. honeycomb tripe	½ tsp. pepper
1 slice bacon, chopped	¼ tsp. marjoram
2 onions, diced	¼ tsp. thyme
2 carrots, sliced	2 bay leaves
1 green pepper, finely chopped	2 cups beef broth
2 stalks celery, sliced	2 cups white wine
1 veal knuckle, chopped	2 Tbs. tomato paste
1½ tsps. salt	2 Tbs. brandy or Calvados, if you have it

☞ Wash the tripe thoroughly and soak in cold water for one hour, changing the water twice. Spread the bacon, onions, carrots, green pepper, and celery on the bottom of a Dutch oven or heavy casserole. Place the tripe and the veal knuckle over them. Add the salt, pepper, majoram, thyme, bay leaves, broth, and wine. Cover tightly. Bake in a 300-degree oven 6 hours. (You see why I said overnight?) Stir in the tomato paste and brandy. Bake 1 hour longer. Skim all the fat off and serve directly from the casserole.

APPLE BETTY

Serves 6.   Calories per serving: 105.

1 tsp. butter	4 apples, pared and sliced
2 cups cornflakes, crushed	2 Tbs. brown sugar
1 tsp. cinnamon	⅓ cup orange juice
1 tsp. grated lemon rind	1 tsp. Sucaryl

☞ Preheat oven to 375 degrees. Butter a 1-quart casserole. Mix the cornflakes, cinnamon, and lemon rind together. Arrange alternate layers of cornflakes and apples, starting and ending with the cornflakes. Mix the sugar, orange juice, and Sucaryl together. Pour over the top. Bake 30 minutes, or until the apples are tender and the top is browned.

TOTAL CALORIES FOR THE DAY: 630, INCLUDING
59 OF SNACKS

55	*Breakfast*	175	*Lunch*	341	*Dinner*
20	½ cup Mott's 5-Fruit Drink	40	Diet vegetable soup	231	Fish Paprika*
				30	Braised celery
35	1 slice Protegen toast	20	2 Diet-10 crackers	30	Beets
	Black coffee	65	1 small apple	15	Cucumber salad
1	Midmorning drink	50	½ oz. Camembert cheese	35	Snow pudding* Black coffee
			Tea with lemon	58	Try a little yogurt if the skim milk is monotonous.
			Midafternoon tea		

FISH PAPRIKA

Serves 6. Calories per serving: 231 ■ Feeling Hungarian today? You'll soon be looking like Zsa Zsa Gabor if you keep counting those calories. Also, fish is supposed to be brain food.

1 lb. carp	Fish stock (recipe follows)
1 lb. whitefish	1½ Tbs. paprika
1 lb. perch	1 green pepper, coarsely chopped
1 Tbs. salt	
2 large onions, finely chopped	

FISH STOCK

1 lb. of fish heads	3 stalks celery, chopped
1 large onion, chopped	2 carrots, chopped
1 Tbs. salt	Water to cover

Combine everything. Simmer 1 hour. Strain.

☞ Cut the fish into 2-inch strips, keeping the 3 kinds separate. Sprinkle with salt. Let stand 1 hour. In bottom of a large casserole or iron kettle sprinkle ⅓ of the chopped onions. Add a layer of one kind of fish. Continue, ending with onion. Pour on enough fish stock to cover ⅔ of the fish and onions. Bring to a boil. Add the paprika and green pepper. Cook until fish flakes. Season to taste and let stand 10 minutes before serving. To serve cold, arrange cooked fish in individual serving dishes. Pour on the fish stock. Chill until jellied.

SNOW PUDDING

Serves 3.   Calories per serving: 35.

1 Tbs. gelatin	1 tsp. Sucaryl
¼ cup cold water	3 oz. lemon juice
1⅓ cups boiling water	½ tsp. lemon rind, grated
1 Tbs. sugar	1 egg white, stiffly beaten

☞ Soften the gelatin in the cold water, add the boiling water, and stir until dissolved. Stir in the sugar, Sucaryl, and lemon juice and rind. Chill until the mixture begins to set. Then beat with a rotary beater until frothy. Fold in the stiffly beaten egg white. Chill in individual molds. Top with a sprig of fresh mint.

TOTAL CALORIES FOR THE DAY: 614, INCLUDING 59 OF SNACKS

25	*Breakfast*	125	*Lunch*	405	*Dinner*
25	½ cup V-8 juice Black coffee	10	Clear chicken broth	350	Broiled lamb chop
1	Midmorning low-calorie drink	106	Chef's salad: ½ oz. Swiss cheese 1 oz. white meat of chicken	15	½ grilled tomato
				15	3 large mushrooms, grilled
		9	Lime D-Zerta Tea with lemon	15	Salad
				10	½ cup rhubarb Black coffee
			Midafternoon tea	58	6 oz. skim milk at bedtime

☞ This is a simple day's cooking: Be sure to cut off all the fat from the lamb chop.

COTTAGE CHEESE WITH HERBS

☞ ¼ cup cottage cheese per person. Mix well with lots of chopped chives, parsley, and basil. Arrange prettily on a lettuce leaf.

TOTAL CALORIES FOR THE DAY: 6 3 0, INCLUDING
5 9 OF SNACKS

70	*Breakfast*	101	*Lunch*	400	*Dinner*
70	Scrambled egg	25	4 oz. hot V-8	300	Lamb stew*
	Black coffee		juice	50	Cottage cheese
1	Midmorning	50	Grapefruit		with herbs*
	drink		sections on	50	Fresh
			chicory		pineapple
		26	Jellied prune		Black coffee
			whip (page		
			97)	58	6 oz. skim milk
			Tea with lemon		at bedtime
			Midafternoon tea		

LAMB STEW

Serves 4. Calories per serving: 300. ■ *We never liked lamb stew before we found this combination of flavors.*

1½ lbs. lamb shoulder, cut in
    2-inch squares
    Salt and pepper, MSG
6 scallions, tops chopped but
    not bottoms
6 very young carrots, sliced
2 turnips, diced

1 clove garlic
1 cup white wine
2 cups beef bouillon
¼ tsp. thyme
½ tsp. marjoram
1 bay leaf

☞ Season the lamb with salt and pepper and brown in your Teflon pan. Place the browned lamb and all the cut-up vegetables and the clove of garlic (which has been put through a garlic press) in a deep casserole. Pour in the wine and bouillon and mix well. Cover tightly and simmer in a 375-degree oven for 1¼ hours.

TOTAL CALORIES FOR THE DAY: 665, INCLUDING
59 OF SNACKS

84	*Breakfast*	195	*Lunch*	327	*Dinner*
12	4 oz. cranberry juice	135	Cheese soufflé (page 25)	250	Broiled hamburger
50	½ cup Cream of Wheat	15	Watercress	25	Spinach purée*
22	2 oz. skim milk Black coffee	45	½ cup diet apricots Tea with lemon	25	Grated carrot salad*
				27	½ cup fresh strawberries Black coffee
1	Midmorning drink		Midafternoon tea		
				58	6 oz. skim milk at bedtime

SPINACH PURÉE

Serves 2. Calories per serving: 25.

> 1 pkg. frozen chopped spinach
> 1 Tbs. chives, chopped
> 1 Tbs. lemon juice
>
> 1 Tbs. plain yogurt
> Speck of nutmeg
> Salt and pepper

☞ Cook spinach as directed on package. Drain well. Place in blender with other ingredients. Blend about ½ minute and serve immediately.

GRATED CARROT SALAD

☞ Grate raw carrots and mix with Marzetti's diet coleslaw dressing. Nestle a couple of tablespoons into a lettuce cup.

TOTAL CALORIES FOR THE DAY: 508, INCLUDING 59 OF SNACKS

20 *Breakfast*	139 *Lunch*	290 *Dinner*
20 Mott's 5-Fruit Drink	35 1 slice Protegen toast	105 Calves' liver*
Black coffee	95 1 oz. Cheddar cheese spread	60 Eggplant and zucchini*
1 Midmorning drink	9 Orange D-Zerta	50 Jellied apple, beet, and celery salad*
	Midafternoon tea	75 Pears belle Hélène*
		Black coffee
		58 6 oz. skim milk at bedtime

CALVES' LIVER

Serves 4.   Calories per serving: 105.

1 lb. calves' liver, sliced ½ inch thick	1 Tbs. parsley, minced
½ cup low-calorie Italian dressing	1 clove garlic, pressed
	1 tsp. onion, grated

☞ Marinate the liver for several hours in a mixture of the rest of the ingredients. Drain the liver but save the marinade. Brown liver in Teflon pan about 3 minutes on each side. Turn off heat until liver attains desired state of doneness. Transfer meat to warm platter, stir the marinade into the skillet, and heat. Pour over the liver and serve immediately.

[*continued*]

EGGPLANT AND ZUCCHINI

Serves 4.   Calories per serving: 60.

1 small eggplant, peeled and
   sliced in ¼-inch pieces
2 medium zucchini, peeled
   and sliced in ¼-inch
   pieces
2 onions, peeled and sliced
   thin

1 cup celery, diced
1 clove of garlic
1¼ cups tomato juice
2 tsps. Worcestershire sauce
1½ tsps. salt
Pinch oregano

☞ Arrange the vegetables in alternate layers in a casserole. Mix the other ingredients together and pour over the vegetables. Cover well and cook in a 325-degree oven for 1½ hours.

JELLIED APPLE, BEET, AND CELERY SALAD

Serves 3.   Calories per serving: 50.

1 envelope D-Zerta lemon
   gelatin
¾ cup hot water
¼ cup beet juice
Few drops red food coloring
¼ Tbs. vinegar

½ tsp. salt
Dash pepper
½ cup diced canned beets
¼ cup celery, chopped
1 medium apple, peeled,
   cored, and diced

☞ Dissolve the gelatin in hot water and stir in the beet juice, food coloring, vinegar, salt, and pepper. Cool and stir in the beets, celery, and apples. Pour into molds and chill until firm.

PEARS BELLE HÉLÈNE

☞ Use 2 halves dietetic canned pears, 2 tablespoons dietetic vanilla ice cream, and 2 tablespoons Diet Delite chocolate sauce per serving.

TOTAL CALORIES FOR THE DAY: 616, INCLUDING 59 OF SNACKS

256	*Breakfast*	21	*Lunch*	280	*Dinner*
211	½ kippered herring* on	12	Vegetable broth	135	Crabmeat à la Palace*
45	Diet toast Black coffee	9	Lemon D-Zerta Tea with lemon	20	Green beans with mush-rooms
1	Midmorning drink		Midafternoon tea	15	Mixed green salad
				110	Cherries Jubilee*
				58	6 oz. skim milk at bedtime

KIPPERED HERRING

☞ After you warm your herring in a skillet, place it gently on a paper towel and blot gently to remove as much oil as you possibly can. Serve with a generous wedge of lemon. If you can't face a herring at this hour—and there are many who can't—have a boiled egg, and eat some sardines for lunch.

Time to make soup again.

CRABMEAT À LA PALACE

Calories per serving: 135.

☞ That's the old Palace in San Francisco. Main difference is the mayonnaise. You can get canned artichoke bottoms at
[*continued*]

specialty food shops or write to Bloomingdale's in New York. There are two different sizes, large and small. Use 3 if small, 2 if large. Mix fresh back-fin lump crabmeat with some low-calorie mayonnaise diluted with fresh lemon juice. Pile artistically on the artichoke bottoms, garnish with green pepper rings and radishes. If it is a cold, damp night, this can be heated in the oven. Otherwise, serve it cold.

GREEN BEANS AND MUSHROOMS

Just add a can of sliced mushrooms to the green beans and heat.

CHERRIES JUBILEE

Serves 6. Calories per serving: 110.

1 large can diet pitted Bing cherries	Dash nutmeg
½ tsp. Sucaryl	¼ cup brandy
¼ tsp. cinnamon	6 small scoops diet vanilla ice cream

☞ Drain the cherries, reserving ½ cup of the liquid. To this liquid add Sucaryl, cinnamon, and nutmeg. Place cherries in a heatproof dish over a burner and pour liquid over it. Keep the flame low; this must warm slowly and never come to a simmer. Place ice cream in 6 sherbet glasses. Heat the brandy and pour over the cherries and light. When the flame dies, spoon the cherries over the ice cream.

TOTAL CALORIES FOR THE DAY: 676, INCLUDING
59 OF SNACKS

117	**Breakfast**	177	**Lunch**	323	**Dinner**
50	½ grapefruit	135	Cheese soufflé	235	Veal chop
45	½ cup oatmeal		(page 25)		casserole*
22	2 oz. skim milk	12	Watercress	20	½ cup broccoli
	Black coffee	30	1 fresh plum	18	Marinated
			Tea with lemon		green bean
1	Midmorning				salad
	snack		Midafternoon	50	1 small bunch
			tea		seedless
					grapes
					Black coffee
				58	6 oz. skim milk
					at bedtime

VEAL CHOP CASSEROLE

Serves 3.   Calories per serving: 235. ■ *If you prepare this in the morning and then refrigerate it, you can get every last bit of fat off, and think how thin you'll be.*

1 tsp. salt	½ onion
¼ tsp. pepper	½ cup white wine
⅛ tsp. dried thyme	¼ cup beef broth
½ Tbs. butter	½ garlic clove, pressed
3 veal chops, 2 inches thick	Small bay leaf
⅛ tsp. dry breadcrumbs	2 sprigs parsley
2 cloves	¼ cup chopped scallions

☞ Mix the salt, pepper, and thyme and dust on chops. Melt the butter in a casserole and brown the chops lightly on both

[*continued*]

sides. Stir in the breadcrumbs and let them brown a little. Stick the cloves into the onion and add to the rest of the casserole with the wine, broth, garlic, bay leaf, parsley, and scallions. Cover tightly. Bake in a 375-degree oven for 45 minutes. Remove the cover and bake 15 minutes longer. Skim off the fat and serve directly from the casserole.

TOTAL CALORIES FOR THE DAY: 640, INCLUDING 59 OF SNACKS

	Breakfast		*Lunch*		*Dinner*
66		115		400	
31	2 oz. cranberry juice, 2 oz. orange juice	100	Chicken livers en brochette*	25	Chicken egg drop soup*
35	1 slice Protegen toast	15	Mixed green salad	220	Chicken chow mein*
	Black coffee		Tea with lemon	100	½ cup rice
1	Midmorning drink		Midafternoon bouillon	55	Fresh pineapple spears (save the shells for the day after tomorrow)
					Jasmine tea
				58	6 oz. skim milk at bedtime

CHICKEN LIVERS EN BROCHETTE

Calories per serving: 100. ■ *Use 2 ounces chicken livers per person.*

☞ Get out the skewers again! Marinate the chicken livers in Italian diet salad dressing diluted with fresh lemon juice. Depends on the size of the livers how many you can have. Weigh them up on your postal scale. Slip them on the skewers with fresh mushrooms and cherry tomatoes and inch-square pieces of green pepper. Very colorful. Broil until the chicken livers are done, about 6 minutes, turning once.

CHICKEN EGG DROP SOUP

☞ You might as well make the soup from scratch because you need cooked chicken for the chow mein. So make some chicken soup—you know: onion, celery, salt, pepper, chicken. Poach gently until the chicken is tender. Place in the refrigerator after straining and let the fat harden so you can get it off. When you are ready to have dinner, bring your chicken broth to a boil. Beat up an egg in a teacup, swirl the boiling soup mightily with your spoon and pour in the egg. Gets all streaky and thickens the soup slightly. One egg for 3 servings.

CHICKEN CHOW MEIN

Serves 6. Calories per serving: 220. ■ *This one will freeze nicely, so make enough for 6 and you'll have some tucked away for when you don't feel like cooking.*

[continued]

2 Tbs. oil

2 onions, sliced

2 cups celery, sliced

¾ lb. mushrooms, sliced

1½ cups chicken broth

1 cup water chestnuts

1 cup bean sprouts

½ cup bamboo shoots

1 Tbs. cornstarch

3 Tbs. soy sauce

3 cups sliced cooked chicken

3 cups cooked fine egg
    noodles

☞ Heat the oil in your trusty wok, sauté the onions 10 minutes, stirring frequently. Add the celery, mushrooms, and broth. Cook over low heat 5 minutes. Stir in the water chestnuts, bean sprouts, and bamboo shoots. Cook 3 minutes. Mix the cornstarch and soy sauce to a smooth paste. Stir into the skillet and stir constantly until thickened. Add the chicken, taste for seasoning, and serve when the chicken is heated through.

Meanwhile, on the back of the stove, you have been cooking the noodles.

This is also an excellent way to use leftover turkey.

TOTAL CALORIES FOR THE DAY: 644, INCLUDING
59 OF SNACKS

12	*Breakfast*	205	*Lunch*	368	*Dinner*
12	4 oz. cranberry juice	55	½ can Campbell's tomato soup	143	Filet of sole Almondine*
	Black coffee			35	Stewed tomatoes
		65	1 small apple		Louisiana
1	Midmorning drink	85	1 oz. Camembert cheese	55	½ cup peas
			Tea with lemon	35	Coleslaw
				100	Lemon ice
			Midafternoon tea		Black coffee
				58	6 oz. skim milk at bedtime

FILET OF SOLE ALMONDINE

Serves 4.   Calories per serving: 143.

☞ Broil 4 ounces of filet of sole per person, after brushing the sole with diet Italian dressing. Melt 1 tablespoon butter in a pan and brown in it 2 almonds per person, sliced paper-thin. It is astonishing how many slices you can get from an almond. While browning the almonds, don't even blink or they will burn. Sprinkle over the sole with salt, pepper, and paprika.

Get Italian lemon ice from the little man at the corner. He's probably Greek.

The stewed tomatoes just have celery, onions, and green pepper diced up and cooked with them.

TOTAL CALORIES FOR THE DAY: 611, INCLUDING 59 OF SNACKS

66	*Breakfast*	146	*Lunch*	340	*Dinner*
20	½ cup Mott's 5-Fruit Drink	100	Fruit salad in pineapple shell*	240	Sauerbraten*
46	1 slice Holly-wood Dark diet toast Black coffee	46	D-Zerta butterscotch pudding Tea with lemon	30	Red cabbage*
				30	Waldorf salad
				40	Apricot whip* Black coffee
1	Midmorning drink		Midafternoon refreshment	58	6 oz. skim milk at bedtime

FRUIT SALAD IN PINEAPPLE SHELL

Serves 2. Calories per serving: 100.

☞ If you had been prudent several days ago, you still have the pineapple shells, carefully wrapped in plastic, in your refrigerator. Take some of the pineapple, a couple of strawberries, half an apple, a couple of grapefruit sections, some seedless grapes, and a couple of orange sections. Arrange all this in the shell. Looks beautiful, doesn't it?

SAUERBRATEN

Serves 10. Calories per serving: 240. ■ *Can be frozen.*

4 lb. pot roast, whatever cut you prefer	1½ cups vinegar
1 Tbs. cooking oil	½ cup red wine
	1 cup water

¾ tsp. Sucaryl

12 whole cloves

½ tsp. peppercorns

1 tsp. mustard seeds

4 bay leaves

¼ cup crushed ginger snaps

3 onions, peeled and sliced

☞ Combine all ingredients except the ginger snaps in a large bowl. Refrigerate for two days, turning the meat occasionally. Remove the meat from the marinade, drain well, and towel dry. Heat the oil in a Dutch oven and brown the meat. Add ¾ cup of the marinade and simmer until tender, 3½ to 4 hours. Add the remaining marinade. Remove the meat to a hot platter. Quick-freeze the drippings to remove the fat. Heat gravy and stir in the ginger-snap crumbs until smooth. Serve with the meat.

RED CABBAGE

Serves 3.   Calories per serving: 30.

1 Tbs. bacon drippings

2 tsps. Sucaryl

2 Tbs. onion, chopped

1½ Tbs. vinegar

3 cups red cabbage, shredded

1 tsp. caraway seed

☞ Melt fat and sauté the onion lightly. Add the other ingredients and cabbage and cook, covered, for 20 minutes over low heat.

APRICOT WHIP

Serves 3.   Calories per serving: 40.

☞ Drain the juice from a can of diet apricots and place apricots in blender. Beat the whites of three eggs until stiff, fold in apricots, and serve.

TOTAL CALORIES FOR THE DAY: 595½,
INCLUDING 58 OF SNACKS

25 *Breakfast*	137½ *Lunch*	375 *Dinner*
25 ½ cup tomato juice	12½ No-account borscht	295 Veal Marsala*
Black coffee	125 Shrimp salad* in tomato	20 Italian green beans
Midmorning drink		60 Cottage cheese dessert*
	Tea with lemon	Black coffee
	Midafter-noon tea	58 6 oz. skim milk at bedtime

The no-account borscht recipe is on page 12. You should have broth left over for several days. Freeze it in 1-cup containers for later use.

SHRIMP SALAD

☞ For this, we discovered Pacific Pearl at the A & P. They are crisp little shrimp, very low in calories. With a little diet mayonnaise, zipped up with some mustard or curry, if you have East Indian leanings, they fit nicely in a smallish tomato.

VEAL MARSALA

Serves 4.   Calories per serving: 295.

1 Tbs. cooking oil
1 clove garlic, pressed
1 lb. thin-cut (scaloppini) veal

½ cup grated Parmesan cheese
¼ lb. fresh mushrooms, sliced thin

¼ cup Marsala	1 tsp. salt
⅛ tsp. oregano	⅛ tsp. pepper
½ tsp. paprika	

☞ Heat the oil in the Teflon pan and put in garlic. Coat the meat with the cheese and brown on both sides. Add the remaining ingredients and cook, covered, for 20 minutes. (We have a gentleman friend who cooks as a hobby. This dish he can make, he says, drunk or sober.)

COTTAGE CHEESE DESSERT

Serves 3.   Calories per serving: 60.

½ lb. uncreamed cottage	½ Tbs. cornmeal
cheese	Pinch of salt
3 Tbs. buttermilk	½ Tbs. Sucaryl
2 eggs, beaten	¼ tsp. vanilla
¼ tsp. cornstarch	¼ tsp. rum

☞ Blend the cheese and buttermilk in blender until smooth. Remove to bowl and add the eggs, beating well. Add the cornstarch, cornmeal, salt, Sucaryl, vanilla, and rum and beat them all together. Preheat oven to 350 degrees. Lightly grease a small pie pan and pour the mixture into it. Bake 25 minutes, or until lightly browned.

TOTAL CALORIES FOR THE DAY: 672, INCLUDING
59 OF SNACKS

116 *Breakfast*	200 *Lunch*	297 *Dinner*
70 Poached egg on	130 Calves' liver	140 Barbecued
46 Diet toast	(page 8)	spareribs*
Black coffee	with bacon	32 1 cup sauer-
	and onion	kraut
1 Midmorning	20 Spinach	40 Harvard beets*
drink	50 ½ grapefruit	20 French endive
	Tea with lemon	with diet
		dressing
	Midafternoon	65 Baked apple
	bouillon	Black coffee
		58 6 oz. buttermilk
		(fooled you!)
		at bedtime

BARBECUED SPARERIBS

Serves 3.   Calories per serving: 140.

2½ lbs. spareribs	¼ cup low-calorie applesauce
½ cup soy sauce	2 cloves of garlic, pressed
1 tsp. Sucaryl	½ Tbs. salt

☞ Cut the ribs into serving pieces. Place in a shallow roasting pan, meaty side up. Prepare sauce by combining the rest
of the ingredients. Pour over the ribs and allow to marinate
in the refrigerator for several hours. Bake in a 350-degree oven,
covered, for 1 hour. Uncover and baste frequently for the next
½ hour.

HARVARD BEETS

☞ Just substitute Sucaryl for sugar in your old recipe. Use just enough cornstarch to thicken the juice. No problems here.

TOTAL CALORIES FOR THE DAY: 614, INCLUDING 59 OF SNACKS

72	*Breakfast*	123	*Lunch*	360	*Dinner*
50	½ cup Cream Wheat	100	Whole large artichoke vinaigrette (page 18)	160	Stuffed lobster tails* (page 76)
22	2 oz. skim milk			30	Broiled tomato halves
	Black coffee	23	Diet pears	20	Broccoli
			Tea with lemon	15	Mixed green salad
1	Midmorning drink		Midafternoon tea	135	Cheese cake*
					Black coffee
				58	How about some yogurt?

CHEESE CAKE

Serves 8.   Calories per serving: 145. ■ *Can be frozen.*

3 eggs, separated
1 lb. farmer cheese
6 Tbs. Sucaryl
1 Tbs. vanilla
1 Tbs. sugar
¼ tsp. cinnamon

CRUST
½ cup graham cracker crumbs
1 Tbs. softened butter
½ tsp. Sucaryl

[continued]

☞ To make the crust, mix the crumbs, butter, and Sucaryl and press against the sides of a small spring-form pan. For the cake itself, place the egg yolks, cheese, 6 teaspoons Sucaryl, sugar, vanilla, and cinnamon in the electric blender. Blend until smooth and creamy. Scrape the mixture into a bowl and fold in the egg whites which have been beaten until peaks have formed. Pour the mixture into the spring-form pan and place in a preheated 325-degree oven for 15 minutes. Turn oven to 450 degrees and bake 5 minutes more. Remove from oven. Can be glazed with fresh fruit.

TOTAL CALORIES FOR THE DAY: 631, INCLUDING
59 OF SNACKS

50	*Breakfast*	157	*Lunch*	365	*Dinner*
12	4 oz. low calorie cranberry juice	55	½ can Campbell's chicken soup with rice	175	Sarasota lamb shanks*
36	1 slice gluten toast with diet jam			100	½ cup brown rice
		25	Spiced apple and grape salad*	25	½ cup kohlrabi
	Black coffee			15	Mixed green salad
1	Midmorning low-calorie drink	43	½ oz. Camembert cheese	50	Baked grapefruit*
		34	on 2 slices Melba toast		Black coffee
			Tea with lemon	58	6 oz. skim milk at bedtime
			Midafternoon tea		

SPICED APPLE AND GRAPE SALAD

Serves 2.   Calories per serving: about 25.

☞ Combine contents of 1 Strawberry Flavor D-Zerta with a dash of salt cinnamon and nutmeg. Add 1 cup boiling water, stir to dissolve. Chill until slightly thickened. Fold in ⅓ cup diced peeled apple and 1½ tablespoons seeded cut grapes. Chill in molds until firm. Unmold on crisp greens.

SARASOTA LAMB SHANKS

Serves 4.   Calories per serving: 175.

[continued]

☞ The little old lady—you see, I no longer refer to her as the fat little old lady—soon got to feeling so good that when I telephoned her one day to find out how things were going she said, "Remember that recipe with the lamb shanks we liked so much? Couldn't we reduce the calories in that one?" She sent the recipe up and I went right to work on it. Hardly had to make any changes at all. This is the most economical recipe in the book. Every time you have a leg of lamb get the butcher to cut off the shank. Put it in a plastic bag and freeze it and when you have four, or however many people you have to serve, get it out of the freezer.

4 lamb shanks	1 tsp. paprika
1 Tbs. butter	1 tsp. powdered ginger
2 onions, sliced	1 tsp. salt
½ cup dry white wine	½ tsp. pepper
½ cup tomato juice	1 cup fat free chicken broth

☞ Remove all fat from the lamb shanks. Melt the butter in the Teflon pan and brown the shanks well on all sides. Place them in a casserole. In the Teflon pan sauté 2 sliced onions, then add the white wine, tomato juice, paprika, ginger, salt, pepper, and chicken broth. Cook and stir for a few minutes, then pour it over the lamb shanks in the casserole. Cover and bake in a 250-degree oven for 3 hours or until tender, when the meat will come free from the bone easily. Skim any fat from the top. If you do this the day before you can really get every speck of fat off, then just reheat before serving.

BAKED GRAPEFRUIT

☞ Sprinkle some Sucaryl on a half of grapefruit and bake until warm. Easy.

TOTAL CALORIES FOR THE DAY: 623, INCLUDING
59 OF SNACKS

57	*Breakfast*	160	*Lunch*	347	*Dinner*
20	½ cup Mott's 5-Fruit Drink	95	Shrimp salad (page 10)	280	Sirloin steak*
35	1 slice gluten toast	65	1 small orange Tea with lemon	20	Spinach
2	Low-calorie jam Black coffee			35	Artichoke hearts vinaigrette on watercress
			Midafternoon tea		
1	Midmorning drink			12	Coffee sparkle* Black coffee
				58	6 oz. skim milk at bedtime

SIRLOIN STEAK

Serves 3. Calories per serving: 280.

2 lbs. sirloin steak
1 clove of garlic, pressed
½ Tbs. olive oil
¾ tsp. Worcestershire sauce
½ tsp. prepared mustard
Salt and pepper to taste
MSG

☞ Remove all visible fat and slash edges of steak every two inches, which keeps it from curling up. Mix the remaining ingredients and rub well into the meat on both sides. Let stand at room temperature for 4 hours. Preheat the broiler and place the steak 1½ inches from the flame. Broil on both sides, allowing 5 minutes to the side until desired doneness. (This timing is purely personal, and you must test by cutting from time to time if you don't know exactly how long. Much depends on the thickness of the steak.)

[*continued*]

COFFEE SPARKLE

Serves 3.   Calories per serving: 12.

1 envelope unflavored gelatin	2 tsps. Sucaryl
¼ cup cold water	¼ tsp. vanilla
1¾ cups freshly brewed strong coffee	Dash of salt

☞ Soften the gelatin in cold water in a small bowl. Stir in hot coffee until the gelatin dissolves. Add Sucaryl, vanilla, and salt. Pour into small shallow pan. Chill 2 hours, until firm. Break gelatin up with a fork or put through a potato ricer. Spoon into parfait glasses. Top if you wish with a thin ribbon of orange peel that has been tied in a loose knot.

TOTAL CALORIES PER DAY: 709, INCLUDING 59 OF SNACKS

47	*Breakfast*	104	*Lunch*	499	*Dinner*
12	½ cup diet cranberry juice	80	Deviled egg (page 31) on watercress with	174	Cioppino*
				150	2 pieces 1-inch-thick Italian bread
35	1 slice diet toast Black coffee	15	Radishes, cucumber, and onion slices	75	Caesar salad*
1	Midmorning drink			100	Fresh fruit cup Black coffee
		9	Lime D-Zerta Tea with lemon	58	6 oz. skim milk at bedtime
			Midafternoon tea		

CIOPPINO (FISH STEW)

Serves 6.   Calories per serving: 174.   ■   *Can be frozen.*

1 Tbs. olive oil	¼ tsp. pepper
2 cloves garlic, pressed	4 drops Tabasco
1 large onion, diced	2 cups clam broth
1 green pepper, diced	1 lb. shrimp
2 carrots, grated	2 cans crabmeat
¼ cup chopped parsley	1 cup oysters
1 large can tomatoes	½ lb. filet of sole, cut in 1-inch
2 bay leaves	pieces
Salt	

☞ In a 3-quart saucepan, sauté in olive oil the garlic, onion, green pepper, and carrots for 3 to 5 minutes. Add parsley, tomatoes, bay leaves, salt, pepper, Tabasco, and clam broth. Simmer for 15 minutes. Add everything else and cook for 15 minutes more. Serve at once. And you've just got to have the Italian bread—after the little you've had to eat all day, it ought to taste like heaven.

CAESAR SALAD

Serves 3.   Calories per serving: 75.

☞ In the bottom of a wooden salad bowl crush a clove or two of garlic with the salt and pepper. Add 1 teaspoon prepared mustard. Smash in 2 anchovies. Pour in 2 tablespoons olive oil. Squeeze in the juice of a whole lemon. Pile in crisp cold romaine which has been broken into bite-size pieces. Break over the whole thing an egg that has been coddled for 1 minute and toss, toss, toss, until every leaf is well coated. I'm sorry you can't have the fried croutons, but you've had a marvelous dinner—and, after all, isn't this a diet?

TOTAL CALORIES FOR THE DAY: 644, INCLUDING
59 OF SNACKS

72	*Breakfast*	135	*Lunch*	378	*Dinner*
50	½ oz. cornflakes	125	Mushroom	287	Chicken
22	2 oz. skim milk		soufflé*		Hawaiian*
	Black coffee	10	Watercress	49	Vegetable
1	Midmorning		salad		medley*
	drink		Tea with lemon	15	Mixed green
			Midafternoon		salad
			drink	27	½ cup fresh
					strawberries
					Black coffee
				58	6 oz. skim milk
					at bedtime

MUSHROOM SOUFFLÉ

Serves 3. Calories per serving: 125. ■ *Full credit to the
little old lady, who dreamed up this one all by herself.*

1 can diet mushroom soup	1 Tbs. butter
3 eggs, separated	Pepper and salt
10 small mushrooms	

☞ Put the diet soup in the blender in its condensed state.
Do *not* dilute. Sauté the mushrooms in the butter in the Teflon
pan until they are brown and soft. Transfer to blender. Mix
on low speed. Meanwhile, beat the egg whites until they form
soft peaks. Put the egg yolks into the blender with the other
things. Fold the blender mixture gently into the egg whites,
season, and put the wrole schmear into a soufflé dish with
straight sides. Bake 40 minutes in a 350-degree oven. Serve immediately.

CHICKEN HAWAIIAN

Serves 2.   Calories per serving: 287.

1 broiler-fryer, split	½ cup water
1 small onion, chopped fine	2 slices diet-pack pineapple
¼ cup soy sauce	1 Tbs. parsley, chopped

☞ Arrange chicken skin side down in a shallow baking pan. Mix onion, soy sauce, and water in a bowl, then pour over the chicken. Bake in a 350-degree oven for 45 minutes. Turn chicken. Baste several times with the pan juices. Bake 45 minutes longer, until richly brown and tender. Drain the pineapple slices well on a paper towel. Roll the edge of each slice in finely chopped parsley. Place on top of chicken before serving.

VEGETABLE MEDLEY

Serves 3.   Calories per serving: 49.

½ Tbs. salad oil	1 cup spinach leaves,
1½ cups celery, thinly sliced	coarsely chopped
1 cup cut green beans	½ tsp. salt
2 cups Chinese cabbage,	¼ tsp. pepper
coarsely chopped	¼ cup water

☞ Heat salad oil in wok or large skillet. Stir in celery and green beans. Sauté lightly, stirring constantly, 2 or 3 minutes. Add cabbage and spinach. Toss well over heat until well mixed. Sprinkle with salt and pepper. Pour water over. Cover and steam 10 minutes, or until just crisply tender.

TOTAL CALORIES FOR THE DAY: 550, INCLUDING
59 OF SNACKS

27	*Breakfast*	109	*Lunch*	355	*Dinner*
27	½ cup fresh strawberries	0	Meat soup stock (page 54)	300	Beef Stew Wilkerson*
	Black coffee			25	Large salad
		100	Crabmeat salad	30	2 fresh plums
1	Midmorning low-calorie drink	9	Lemon D-Zerta Tea with lemon		Black coffee
			Midafternoon tea	58	6 oz. skim milk at bedtime

Time to make vegetable broth again. You can use it for your midmorning break. Freeze it in 1-cup servings and you'll have it handy any time you want it. It is also excellent when the children get the "Throwing-up bug." Stays down when nothing else does.

Be sure to use diet mayonnaise in the salad, with ¾ cup of crabmeat. We like to add a teaspoon of Dijon mustard to a tablespoon of Mayo 7. Gives it a real zing.

BEEF STEW WILKERSON

Serves 6. Calories per serving: 300. ■ *The main problem with this recipe is to find the pickled walnuts. Make it without them if you really can't locate them—it still tastes good.*

1½ lbs. lean round steak
1 Tbs. butter
3 medium onions, quartered
1 clove crushed garlic
3 large carrots in 1-inch slices
2 white turnips quartered

5 stalks celery
bouquet garni
6 pickled walnuts
3 pints beef stock
1 4½ oz. jar sliced mushrooms

☞ Cut the meat in ¾ inch cubes. In the trusty Teflon pan melt the butter and brown the meat on all sides to seal in the juices. Remove meat from pan and replace with the garlic and onions, and cook them until they are golden. Place the meat and onions in a casserole with a lid. Pour in the beef stock and add the rest of the vegetables, 6 pickled walnuts, and the bouquet garni (a bay leaf, 2 sprigs parsley, a dozen peppercorns, a pinch of thyme, and pinch of marjoram tied up in a cheese-cloth bag). Simmer in a 350-degree oven for an hour and a half, until the meat is tender but not falling apart. Remove the stew from the oven and correct the seasoning. Add a tablespoon of pickled walnut juice, and salt and pepper. If the color seems light, use some Kitchen Bouquet or Gravy Master. Once you have the seasoning right make a small roux (a teaspoon of butter rolled with enough flour to make it stick together). Add the roux to the casserole, stir until thick-ened, and decorate the top with 6 more pickled walnuts. Re-move the bouquet garni (I always put a long string on mine and let it trail over the edge because it is very hard to find).

TOTAL CALORIES FOR THE DAY: 631, INCLUDING
59 OF SNACKS

72	*Breakfast*	225	*Lunch*	275	*Dinner*
50	½ cup oatmeal	150	Western omelet	145	Filet of
22	2 oz. skim milk		(page 50)		flounder
	Black coffee	10	Watercress		Portuguese*
		65	1 sliced orange	20	Fresh asparagus
1	Midmorning		Tea with lemon	20	Squash
	drink			15	Salad
			Midafternoon	75	Whipped
			tea		applesauce*
					Black coffee
				58	6 oz. skim milk
					at bedtime

FILET OF FLOUNDER PORTUGUESE

Serves 2.   Calories per serving: 145.

¾ lb. flounder filets	1 tsp. vinegar
2 onions, finely minced	1 Tbs. parsley, chopped
1 cup tomato juice	1 lemon rind, grated

☞ Place filets in baking dish and cover with onions, tomato
juice, vinegar, and parsley. Bake in hot (450-degree) oven for
15 minutes. Sprinkle with grated lemon rind and serve.

WHIPPED APPLESAUCE

Serves 2.   Calories per serving: 75.

2 cups diet applesauce   1 egg white, beaten stiff
1 Tbs. currant jelly   Pinch of cinnamon

☞ You can use homemade applesauce for this. While it is hot, add the jelly and beat well. Add the egg white; continue to beat. When all the ingredients are well mixed, put the mixture in champagne or sherbet glasses and sprinkle with cinnamon. Serve chilled.

TOTAL CALORIES FOR THE DAY: 618, INCLUDING
31 OF SNACKS

	Breakfast		*Lunch*		*Dinner*
12		160		415	
12	½ cup cranberry juice	55	1 oz. dried chipped beef	300	Crown roast of lamb*
	Black coffee	50	1 cup defatted cream sauce* on	30	¼ cup green pea purée in
1	Midmorning break	46	Diet toast	30	Whole onion cup*
		9	Raspberry D-Zerta	25	Grapefruit sections on watercress
			Tea with lemon	30	Almond rennet junket
			Midafternoon tea		Black coffee

30   You've had enough milk for today.
Have 30 green Thompson grapes

CREAM SAUCE

Makes 2 cups. Calories per cup: 50.

2 Tbs. Wondra flour	¼ tsp. salt
2 Tbs. instant dry milk	½ tsp. MSG
1 tsp. seasoned salt	½ tsp. white pepper

☞ Mix dry ingredients in a cup. Put 1 pint of water in a fruit jar. Pour dry ingredients on top. Close jar and shake well for a few minutes. Pour into heavy pan. Over high heat, stir constantly to keep from sticking. The sauce will be thick and smooth in 2 minutes.

Add 1 ounce dried chipped beef to cream sauce and serve on hot toast.

CROWN ROAST OF LAMB

Serves 8.   Calories per serving: 300.   ■ *This is the night to have the definitive party. It also calls for a superlative butcher. Have him save the scraps and cut every bit of fat off before grinding them. You will need them for the stuffing. Put a cube of potato on each bone to keep it from charring. Or wrap each one in foil.*

FILLING

1 lb. mushrooms, chopped	¼ tsp. pepper
1 onion, finely chopped	½ tsp. basil
½ cup chopped celery	1 egg, beaten
1 tsp. salt	Ground lamb from bones

☞ Place the crown roast (16 ribs) in a baking pan. Mix all the ingredients and place in the center. Roast in a 450-degree oven for 25 minutes. Pour off the fat. Reduce the heat to 350 degrees. Roast 2½ hours longer, or to desired degree of rareness. Make a small slit near the bone to test. Remove the protective devices and replace with paper frills. Serve 2 ribs and 3 tablespoons of stuffing per serving.

PURÉE OF FRESH PEAS IN WHOLE ONION CUPS

Calories per serving: 60.

☞ Poach large onions until tender. Scoop out the centers. (You can save them and use them in tomorrow's Spanish omelet.) Put fresh green peas which have been cooked in the usual fashion into the blender. Serve ¼ cup per onion.

TOTAL CALORIES FOR THE DAY: 654, INCLUDING 60 OF SNACKS

66	*Breakfast*	178	*Lunch*	350	*Dinner*
20	1 cup rhubarb	125	Spanish	140	Oysters
46	Diet toast		omelet*		Rockefeller*
	Black coffee	10	Watercress	20	Broccoli
		43	½ cup diet	60	Cucumbers
1	Midmorning		peaches		with bacon*
	something		Tea with lemon	20	Salad with
		1	Midafternoon		Roquefort
			drink		dressing
				110	Lime pie with
					gingersnap
					crust*
					Black coffee
				58	6 oz. skim milk
					at bedtime

SPANISH OMELET

Serves 3.   Calories per serving: 125.

	SAUCE
3 eggs	1 small can tomatoes
1 Tbs. water	The insides of last night's
½ tsp. salt	onions
1 Tbs. butter	1 green pepper, chopped

☞ Beat the eggs, water, and salt until just blended. Do not overbeat. Heat the butter in the skillet over low heat until it sizzles. Pour the eggs in and tilt the pan to spread them around. As the eggs begin to set, push them back from the sides of the

pan with a fork to permit the uncooked portion to run under-
neath. Put in the Spanish sauce and fold the omelet over onto
a heated plate.

OYSTERS ROCKEFELLER

Serves 3. Calories per serving: 140.

¼ lb. uncooked spinach	2 drops Tabasco
2 Tbs. parsley, chopped	1 Tbs. dry breadcrumbs
1½ Tbs. onion, chopped	1 Tbs. melted butter
¼ tsp. salt	18 oysters on the half shell
Dash pepper	Anisette

☞ Chop together the spinach, parsley, onion, salt, pepper,
and Tabasco. Stir in the breadcrumbs and butter. Fill a baking
pan with rock salt. Place the oysters on it. Quickly spread each
oyster with some of the spinach mixture. Put 1 drop of Ani-
sette on each one. Bake in a 450-degree oven until the edges
are curled and the tops are brown. Serve immediately.

CUCUMBERS WITH BACON

Serves 4. Calories per serving: 60.

2 large cucumbers, pared and cut in thick slices	1 tsp. butter
	1 tsp. lemon juice
2 slices bacon, cooked until crisp, drained on paper towel	Pinch sugar
	Salt and pepper to taste

☞ Cook the cucumbers in 1 inch of lightly salted water for
15 minutes or until barely tender. Drain and combine with the
crumbled bacon and the remaining ingredients. Serve hot.

[continued]

LIME PIE WITH GINGERBREAD CRUST

Serves 8.   Crust: 60 calories per serving. Filling: 50 calories per serving.

CRUST

12 ginger snaps   2 Tbs. melted butter

☞ Crush the ginger snaps into very fine crumbs. Mix with the butter and press against the sides and bottom of an 8-inch pie shell. Since the filling is not baked, prebake the crust in a 375-degree oven for 5 minutes. Cool before filling. Then bake as the recipe directs.

FILLING

1 Tbs. gelatin	¼ tsp. salt
¼ cup cold water	1 tsp. lime or lemon rind,
3 egg yolks	grated
½ cup lime or lemon juice	3 drops green food coloring
2 Tbs. sugar	¼ cup no-fat dry milk
¾ tsp. liquid Sucaryl	2 egg whites

☞ Soften the gelatin in ¼ cup cold water. Beat the egg yolks, lime juice, 1 tablespoon sugar, Sucaryl, and salt in the top of a double boiler. Place over hot water and cook, stirring constantly, until thick. Stir in the gelatin until dissolved. Add the rind and the food coloring. Chill for 20 minutes. Beat the remaining ¼ cup water with the dry milk until the consistency of whipped cream. Beat the egg whites until stiff but not dry and fold in the remaining sugar. Combine with the whipped milk and fold in the lime mixture. Turn into the pie shell. Chill until set. If you like, reserve a few tablespoons of the whipped milk to decorate the top and grate a little rind over it. Freeze half for St. Patrick's Day.

TOTAL CALORIES FOR THE DAY: 637, INCLUDING
31 OF SNACKS

136	*Breakfast*	155	*Lunch*	315	*Dinner*
12	½ cup diet	70	Poached egg	205	Salmon Divan*
	cranberry		Florentine	35	Broiled tomato
	juice		(page 58)	30	Heart of palm
102	¾ cup Wheat	20	1 cup fresh		on watercress
	Chex		cooked	45	Blancmange*
22	2 oz. skim milk		spinach		Black coffee
	Black coffee	65	Whole orange		
			Tea with lemon	30	Small bunch of
1	Midmorning				seedless
	drink		Midafternoon		grapes at
			drink		bedtime

SALMON DIVAN

Serves 3. Calories per serving: 205.

1 pkg. frozen broccoli	2 Tbs. American cheese,
½ Tbs. butter	grated
½ Tbs. flour	1 small can tomatoes, drained
½ tsp. salt	1 can (7¾ oz.) salmon,
Pinch of pepper	drained
½ cup skim milk	1 Tbs. cornflakes, crushed

☞ Preheat oven to 375 degrees. Cook the broccoli as directed on the package. Drain and place in baking dish. Melt the butter in a saucepan, blend in the flour, salt, and pepper. Gradually add the milk, stirring constantly, until it boils. Simmer for 5 minutes. Stir in the cheese and tomatoes. Break the salmon in pieces and place on the broccoli. Pour the sauce

[continued]

over, sprinkle with cornflakes. Place in oven and bake for 30 minutes. Serve directly from the casserole.

BLANCMANGE

Serves 4.　Calories per serving: 45.

1 Tbs. gelatin	1 tsp. liquid Sucaryl
1½ cups skim milk	1 tsp. almond extract
½ Tbs. sugar	Pinch of salt

☞ Soften the gelatin in ½ cup milk. Heat the remaining milk and add the softened gelatin, stirring until dissolved. Add the sugar, Sucaryl, almond extract, and salt. Mix well and cook until syrupy. Beat with a rotary beater or electric mixer until frothy and doubled in quantity. Pour into a mold or individual serving dishes. Chill before serving.

TOTAL CALORIES FOR THE DAY: 687, INCLUDING
61 OF SNACKS

		235	Delicatessen		
20	Breakfast		Lunch	371	Dinner
20	½ cup Mott's 5-Fruit Drink	80	1 slice pumper- nickel bread	310	Veal paprika*
	Black coffee	50	½ oz. slice	19	Zucchini
1	Midmorning drink		Swiss cheese	15	Mixed green salad
		100	2 slices corned beef	27	½ cup fresh strawberries
		5	Pickle		Black coffee
			Tea with lemon	60	½ cup yogurt
			Midafternoon tea		

☞ You can put mustard on your open sandwich. Doesn't count a thing in calories.

VEAL PAPRIKA

Serves 3.   Calories per serving: 310.

1 lb. veal cut in 1-inch pieces	1 onion, finely chopped
½ tsp. salt	1 Tbs. paprika
Pinch pepper	1 cup fat-free chicken broth
1 Tbs. butter	¼ cup yogurt

☞ Season the veal with the salt and pepper. Melt the butter in the Teflon pan. Brown the veal on all sides. Add the onions and brown them. Sprinkle with the paprika and mix well. Add the broth. Cover and cook over low heat 1 hour, or until veal is tender. Stir in the yogurt and heat well, but do not allow to boil or it will curdle.

TOTAL CALORIES FOR THE DAY: 600, INCLUDING
1 OF SNACKS

137	*Breakfast*	119	*Lunch*	343	*Dinner*
50	½ grapefruit	80	6 crab fingers	220	Short ribs
65	½ cup Wheat		with		Kikkoman*
	Chex	20	Marjorie's		with
22	2 oz. skim milk		sauce*	23	½ cup carrots
	Black coffee	10	Watercress	15	Salad
1	Midmorning	9	Lime D-Zerta	85	Lemon cream*
	drink		Tea with lemon		Black coffee
			Midafternoon		Have some no-
			tea		calorie ginger
					ale tonight

MARJORIE'S SAUCE FOR CRAB FINGERS

Calories per tablespoonful: 20.

4 Tbs. diet mayonnaise
2 Tbs. House of Parliament
   sauce

1 Tbs. Bahamian mustard
2 tsps. grated Parmesan cheese
3 drops Tabasco

☞ You have to buy a whole can of crab fingers, so why
don't you have a few people in for drinks—here is your hors
d'ouevre. You must keep your spirits up.

SHORT RIBS KIKKOMAN

Serves 6. Calories per serving: 220. ■ *Can be frozen.*

6 lean short ribs

½ cup Kikkoman soy sauce

1 clove garlic, minced

¼ cup red wine

1 medium onion, chopped

1 8-oz. can tomato sauce

½ cup celery, chopped

½ cup chopped green pepper

¼ tsp. chili powder

¼ tsp. pepper

½ tsp. MSG

☞ Brown short ribs in Teflon pan, then add garlic. Drain fat. Add remaining ingredients and cover tightly. Bake at 325 degrees for 2 hours, or until meat is tender. Carrots may be added for the last ½ hour.

LEMON CREAM

Serves 5.   Calories per serving: 85.

3 lemons

3 whole eggs

2 Tbs. flour

1 tsp. Sucaryl

1 cup water

1 egg white, beaten stiff

☞ Grate the rind of 3 lemons very fine and then squeeze the juice. Beat the whole eggs with a beater, add the rind, the juice, the flour, and the Sucaryl. Heat 1 cup of water to boiling and pour it over the well-beaten mixture. Allow to thicken in the double boiler so that the eggs won't curdle. Remove from the heat but continue stirring until the cream has cooled. Stir in the firmly beaten egg white. Cool in the refrigerator and beat well before serving.

TOTAL CALORIES FOR THE DAY: 601, INCLUDING
59 OF SNACKS

37	*Breakfast*	290	*Lunch*	215	*Dinner*
37	2 oz. orange juice, mixed with 2 oz. cranberry juice	150	Mushroom omelet*	100	Mussels*
		15	Watercress	30	Stewed tomatoes
		125	Cheese-filled Danish*	20	Braised celery (page 38)
	Black coffee		Tea with lemon	15	Endive salad
1	Midmorning drink		Midafternoon drink	50	Broiled grapefruit
					Black coffee
				58	6 oz. skim milk at bedtime

MUSHROOM OMELET

Serves 3. Calories per serving: 150.

☞ Sauté ½ pound of finely sliced mushrooms in a little butter in the Teflon pan until soft and brown. Make a 3-egg omelet and fold the mushrooms in before serving. The reason so many recipes are for 3 is that the cook, who is not on a diet, gets to have two portions and the dieter eats one. Then the cook doesn't have to cook separate meals.

CHEESE-FILLED DANISH

Makes about 32; 125 calories apiece. ■ *You may bake just the number you want and keep the remaining dough for a week in the refrigerator. Or bake them all, then freeze.*

1 pkg. yeast
¼ cup lukewarm water
2 Tbs. sugar
1 tsp. Sucaryl
1 tsp. salt
1¼ cups butter
1 cup hot scalded milk
2 eggs
½ tsp. vanilla
1 tsp. lemon juice

¼ tsp. mace
3½ cups sifted flour

FILLING
1 cup cottage cheese
1 egg yolk
1 Tbs. sugar
¾ tsp. Sucaryl
½ tsp. vanilla

☞ Soften the yeast in the water and stir until dissolved. Combine the sugar, Sucaryl, salt, ¼ cup butter, and milk. Stir until smooth. Cool, then beat in the eggs. Add the yeast, vanilla, lemon juice, mace, and 3 cups of flour. Beat until smooth and add a little more of the flour, if necessary, to make a dough. Cover and let rise in a warm place until double in bulk. Keep remaining butter at room temperature. Roll the dough into a square ¼ inch thick. Dot with half the butter. Fold dough in half and press the edges together. Roll out and dot with the remaining butter. Roll out into a square and fold in quarters. Roll out, fold, and roll again. Fold the dough and place in bowl. Cover and chill 30 minutes. Roll out the dough ⅓ inch thick. Cut into 2½-inch squares; place a tablespoon of the filling on each. Fold two opposite corners to the center and press to seal. Let rise for 30 minutes. Bake in a 475-degree oven 8 minutes. Have the girls in for coffee tomorrow morning. They'll never know you're on a diet.

[*continued*]

MUSSELS

Serves 1.   Calories per serving: 100.

½ qt. mussels	1 clove garlic
½ cup dry white wine	Thyme, bay leaf, parsley
1 small onion, sliced	1 Tbs. flour
½ cup carrots, sliced	½ cup skim milk

☞ Scrub mussels—Scrub, scrub, scrub! Now wash them 3 more times; put vinegar in the last rinse (it makes them spit out the sand). Drain and place in a pan with the rest of the ingredients except milk and flour. When they are all open, remove mussels with a slotted spoon and add flour, mix well, add milk, and bring to a boil.

TOTAL CALORIES FOR THE DAY: 626, INCLUDING 59 OF SNACKS

48	*Breakfast*	84	*Lunch*	435	*Dinner*
12	Cranberry juice	75	Chef's salad with	0	Meat soup
35	Protegen toast		chicken		stock (page
1	Diet jam	9	Raspberry		54)
	Black coffee		D-Zerta	375	Sukiyaki*
			Tea with lemon	60	Watermelon
1	Midmorning	60			(2″ by 2″)
	drink		Midafternoon		Jasmine tea
			drink		
				58	6 oz. skim milk
					at bedtime

☞ Have a can of S. S. Pierce's boned chicken on the shelf. You have a lovely piece of white meat sliced thin over a lot of crisp greens, and there will be some left for later use. You are saving up for tonight.

SUKIYAKI

Serves 3. Calories per serving: 375. ∎ *If you are lucky enough to have a Japanese restaurant in your town, go out to dinner. You should be thin enough now (if you started at the beginning) to sit on the floor and enjoy it. Have the clear soup, sukiyaki, and watermelon—or some other melon if they don't have water. If you are in a backwater or hinterland without such a place, teach yourself to cook Japanese.*

½ Tbs. oil	¼ cup beef broth
¾ lb. sirloin steak cut into	1½ onions, thinly sliced
½-by-2-inch strips	½ cup celery
¼ cup soy sauce	½ cup bamboo shoots, sliced
⅛ tsp. Sucaryl	¼ lb. mushrooms, sliced thin
½ Tbs. sherry	4 sprigs watercress

☞ Heat the oil in a large skillet. Your electric frying pan is good. This can be done right at the table. Brown the meat over high heat, then push to one side. Combine the soy sauce, Sucaryl, sherry, and broth. Pour half the mixture over the meat. Cook the onions and celery in the skillet for 3 minutes, then push them to one side and add the remaining soy-sauce mixture, bamboo shoots, mushrooms, and watercress. Cook 4 minutes. Do not overcook. Serve directly from skillet.

TOTAL CALORIES FOR THE DAY: 647, INCLUDING
36 OF SNACKS

	Breakfast		Lunch		Dinner
28	*Breakfast*	208	*Lunch*	375	*Dinner*
28	½ cup Mott's Apricot Nectar Black coffee	70	Scrambled egg in	200	Frankfurter Hungarian*
		30	Tomato cup* topped with	20	Turnip greens
1	Midmorning drink	14	Crossed anchovies	60	Waldorf salad*
		34	2 Venus wafers	95	Fresh pear Black coffee
		60	D-Zerta butterscotch pudding Tea with lemon	35	½ apple at bedtime
			Afternoon tea		

SCRAMBLED EGG IN TOMATO CUP

Calories per serving: 120.

1 scrambled egg (no butter, use Teflon pan)

1 hollowed-out tomato
2 anchovies, washed and dried

☞ Scramble the egg in the Teflon pan. Early. This has to be cold. Hollow out a tomato, stuff with the egg, and cross two well-washed anchovies on top. Serve prettily on watercress, hot or cold.

FRANKFURTER HUNGARIAN

Serves 3.   Calories per serving: 200.

3 all-beef frankfurters
1 cup sauerkraut
   Small can of peeled
     tomatoes, drained and cut
     up (add the middles you
     took out of the ones for
     lunch).

1 Tbs. parsley, minced
½ tsp. brown sugar
½ tsp. oregano
   Salt and pepper to taste

☞ Cook the frankfurters in water and let them sit a few minutes to get rid of the fat. Remove from water and split in half. Sauté the sauerkraut in the Teflon pan for 5 minutes and add the remaining ingredients. Stir and bring to a simmer. Add the frankfurters and heat through.

WALDORF SALAD

☞ This should be made with diet mayonnaise and about 3 walnuts per serving. Use half an apple per serving.

TOTAL CALORIES FOR THE DAY: 591, INCLUDING
59 OF SNACKS

20	*Breakfast*	112	*Lunch*	400	*Dinner*
20	½ cup rhubarb Black coffee	112	Irish soufflé salad* Tea with lemon	200	4 oz. corned beef (page 27)
1	Midmorning drink		Midafternoon tea	25	1 cup cabbage
				50	Small boiled potato
				15	Mixed green salad
				110	Lime pie (page 130) Black coffee
				58	6 oz. skim milk at bedtime

IRISH SOUFFLÉ SALAD

Serves 4. Calories per serving: 112.   ■   (*Molded tuna fish, if you must know.*)

1 pkg. D-Zerta Lime gelatin	1 cup cottage cheese
1 pkg. D-Zerta Lemon gelatin	½ cup cucumber, grated
1 cup boiling water	3 Tbs. green pepper, chopped
⅓ cup diet mayonnaise	½ Tbs. scallions, chopped
1 Tbs. lemon juice	1 tsp. pimento, chopped
¼ tsp. salt	1 small can water-packed tuna
¼ tsp. Worcestershire sauce	

☞ Combine gelatins and water. Stir until dissolved. Add mayonnaise, lemon juice, salt, and Worcestershire sauce. Beat with rotary beater. Pour into a shallow tray and quick-chill in the freezer until set 1 inch from the edge but still soft in the center. Meanwhile, sieve cottage cheese. Blend in the rest of the ingredients, folding in the tuna and cheese and vegetables. Pour into a mold and chill. Unmold on crisp greens and garnish with green-pepper strips.

TOTAL CALORIES FOR THE DAY: 616, INCLUDING 59 OF SNACKS

90	*Breakfast*	150	*Lunch*	317	*Dinner*
70	1 soft-boiled egg	50	½ cup Campbell's tomato soup	160	Roast turkey
20	½ cup Mott's 5-Fruit Drink			15	½ cup diet cranberry sauce
	Black coffee	100	2 oz. cottage cheese mixed with chopped radishes, onions, and green pepper on 1 slice Hollywood dark bread	80	Sweet potato puff*
1	Midmorning snack			12	Green beans
				15	Salad
				35	Spiced fruit (page 26)
			Tea with lemon		Black coffee
			Midafternoon tea	58	6 oz. skim milk at bedtime

ROAST TURKEY

2 slices 3½" by ¼": 160 calories.

[*continued*]

SWEET POTATO PUFF [PRETEND]

Serves 4.   Calories per serving: 80.

1 pkg. frozen mashed squash
½ tsp. Sucaryl
¼ tsp. maple flavoring
2 Tbs. diet marmalade

2 Tbs. brown sugar
½ tsp. cinnamon
½ tsp. salt
4 pecan halves

☞ Thaw squash in top of double boiler. Add all other ingredients except pecan halves. Blend well. Pour into lightly oiled casserole. Bake for ½ hour in a 350-degree oven.

TOTAL CALORIES FOR THE DAY: 603, INCLUDING 58 OF SNACKS

72	*Breakfast*	183	*Lunch*	290	*Dinner*
50	½ cup corn- flakes	35	Fresh asparagus on	170	Deviled crabmeat*
22	2 oz. skim milk Black coffee	119	Slice of ham with lemon juice	50	Spinach with ½ sliced hard-boiled egg
	Midmorning bouillon	20	1 Tbs. Parme- san cheese	35	½ cup julienne beets
		9	Strawberry D-Zerta Tea with lemon	8	Celery root moutarde*
			Midafternoon tea	27	½ cup fresh strawberries Black coffee
				58	6 oz. skim milk at bedtime

DEVILED CRABMEAT

Serves 3.   Calories per serving: 170.

2 tsps. butter	1 Tbs. Dijon mustard
2 tsps. flour	1 tsp. Worcestershire sauce
½ cup skim milk	2 drops Tabasco
3 Tbs. onion, minced	3 Tbs. dry breadcrumbs
3 Tbs. green pepper, minced	¾ lb. fresh crabmeat
1 tsp. salt	

☞ Make a cream sauce of the butter, flour, and milk, stirring constantly until it boils. Combine the remaining in-

[*continued*]

gredients and mix lightly into the sauce. Spoon into scallop shells. Bake at 400 degrees for 10 minutes, or until lightly browned.

CELERY ROOT MOUTARDE

Serves 4.   Calories per serving: about 8.

☞ Shred 2 cups raw celery root or knob. Marinate in 1 tablespoon Dijon mustard, juice of 2 lemons, and salt for about 2 hours. Arrange on salad plate.

TOTAL CALORIES FOR THE DAY: 678, INCLUDING
58 OF SNACKS

50	*Breakfast*	175	*Lunch*	395	*Dinner*
50	½ grapefruit	100	Crabmeat in	30	Consommé
	Black coffee	30	Tomato shell*		Bellevue*
		45	½ cup diet	250	Turkey Divan*
	Midmorning		apricot	15	Mixed green
	drink		halves		salad
			Tea with lemon	100	Rum Soufflé*
					Black coffee
			Midafternoon		
			no-calorie	58	6 oz. skim milk
			drink		at bedtime

CRABMEAT IN TOMATO SHELL

☞ Mix some crabmeat left over from last night with a little diet mayonnaise flavored with Dijon mustard and stuff in a fresh tomato.

CONSOMMÉ BELLEVUE

Calories per serving: 30.

☞ Combine half clear fat-free chicken broth with half clam juice. Flavor to taste with nutmeg, salt, and pepper.

TURKEY DIVAN

Serves 2. Calories per serving: 250.

[continued]

☞ Cook fresh broccoli until crisply tender and still green. Drain well and place 6 pieces of broccoli in a flat oven dish. Slice white meat of turkey (3 ounces per serving) very thinly and place over the broccoli. Mix 1 can of undiluted diet cream of mushroom soup with 1 tablespoon sherry and pour over the turkey. Sprinkle lightly with Parmesan cheese and heat in the oven until the sauce is bubbling.

GRAND MARNIER SOUFFLÉ

Serves 4.   Calories per serving: 100.

2 egg yolks	1 Tbs. Grand Marnier
¼ cup powdered sugar	4 egg whites
Few grains salt	

☞ Beat yolks until thick and lemon-colored. Add the powdered sugar, few grains salt, and Grand Marnier. Beat egg whites until stiff and dry. Fold into first mixture. Butter a hot omelet pan. Pour in half the mixture, brown, fold, and turn out onto a hot serving dish. Sprinkle with powdered sugar. Cook the remaining mixture the same way. Rum soufflé should be very soft inside. Just before serving, heat another tablespoon of Grand Marnier and pour it over the soufflé and light it. Serve with flourishes.

TOTAL CALORIES FOR THE DAY: 591, INCLUDING
66 OF SNACKS

122	*Breakfast*	94	*Lunch*	309	*Dinner*
50	½ cup unsweetened applesauce	56	Sauerkraut salad*	250	Spring stew*
		21	1 piece Ry-Krisp	15	Mixed green salad
72	½ cup cornflakes with 2 oz. skim milk Black coffee	17	Mocha cream* Iced tea	44	Apricot dessert jelly* Black coffee
			Midafternoon drink	66	Milk punch*
	Midmorning snack				

SAUERKRAUT SALAD

Serves 6. Calories per serving: 56.

2½ cups sauerkraut
4 tomatoes
1 medium green pepper
2 Tbs. sour cream

2 Tbs. low-calorie mayonnaise
1 tsp. onion, grated
4 radishes
Parsley

☞ Chill can of sauerkraut in refrigerator overnight. Drain juice, rinse kraut well in cold water. Slice radishes thinly. Cut pepper into thin strips. Combine all ingredients except tomatoes in large bowl. Mix lightly but thoroughly. Cut tomatoes in narrow wedges. Put 6 of these on each salad plate around a mound of sauerkraut salad. Place sprigs of parsley between tomato wedges.

[*continued*]

MOCHA CREAM

Serves 2.   Calories per serving: 17.

1 tsp. plain gelatin	¾ cup hot coffee
1 Tbs. Diet Delite chocolate syrup	

☞ Soak the gelatin in 1 tablespoon cold water. Stir Diet Delite chocolate syrup into the hot coffee until blended. Add the gelatin and stir until dissolved. Chill in the refrigerator until soupy but not set. Whip with rotary beater or electric mixer until light and frothy. Pour into individual molds and chill until firm. Unmold to serve.

SPRING STEW

Serves 6.   Calories per serving: 250.

1¼ lbs. boneless beef chuck, cut in 1-inch cubes	¼ tsp. savory
1 cup celery, sliced	3 cups water
½ cup onions, chopped	6 small onions
1 tsp. salt	1 lb. new carrots, pared
1 tsp. garlic salt	1 bunch fresh asparagus, cut in 1-inch pieces
⅛ tsp. pepper	¼ cup parsley, chopped
½ tsp. marjoram	2 Tbs. chives, chopped

☞ Brown the beef in your Teflon pan. Add celery, chopped onions, seasonings, and water. Bring to a boil. Cover and simmer 1½ hours, until meat is tender. Add onions and carrots, cover and simmer 15 minutes longer. Add asparagus stalks and cook 8 to 10 minutes, then add asparagus tips, parsley, and chives and cook 5 minutes more. Season with salt and pepper to taste.

APRICOT DESSERT JELLY

Serves 6. Calories per serving: 44.

2 cups drained dietetic
    apricots (3 8-oz. cans)
⅔ cup apricot liquid
1 envelope unflavored gelatin
6 whole cloves

1 cup boiling water
4 tsps. Sucaryl
⅛ tsp. salt
2 tsp. lemon juice

☞ Rub apricots through a sieve or food mill. Mix apricot liquid with gelatin; set aside. Add cloves to boiling water. Stir in softened gelatin until dissolved. Remove from heat. Add the dissolved gelatin, Sucaryl, salt, and lemon juice to sieved apricots. Pour into a 3-cup mold or into 6 individual molds. Chill until firm.

MILK PUNCH

Serves 1. Calories: 66. ■ *I'll bet you are tired of that dreary skim milk. Have a little punch. Enjoy!*

6 oz. skim milk
¼ cup carbonated water

¼ tsp. vanilla or almond
    extract

☞ Put the milk with the flavoring in one glass, the carbonated water in another, and pour from glass to glass to make a frothy mixture.

TOTAL CALORIES FOR THE DAY: 599, INCLUDING 58 OF SNACKS

12	*Breakfast*	145	*Lunch*	384	*Dinner*
12	½ cup diet cranberry juice	105	Oyster stew (page 36)	185	Herb-broiled chicken*
	Black coffee	40	1 tangerine	80	Stewed tomatoes with celery and green peppers
			Tea with lemon		
	Midmorning bouillon		Midafternoon tea	64	½ cup green peas
				15	Salad
				90	Lemon-sherry pudding*
					Black coffee
				58	6 oz. skim milk at bedtime

HERB-BROILED CHICKEN

A quarter-chicken per person. Calories: 185.

2¼	lbs. broiling chicken, cut up	⅛	tsp. marjoram
1	tsp. salt	⅛	tsp. sage
½	tsp. pepper	¼	tsp. paprika
⅛	tsp. thyme	1	Tbs. salad oil
		⅓	cup orange juice

☞ Rinse and dry the chicken. Season with salt and pepper. Crumble herbs into fine powder and add to the oil. Place chicken in a shallow baking pan and brush with herb mixture.

Place under the broiler 4 inches from the heat for 15 minutes. Turn and brush with herb mixture. Broil 10 or 15 minutes longer. Add remaining herbs and orange juice to chicken and bake in a moderate oven (350 degrees) for 35 to 45 minutes or until tender. Baste frequently during the baking.

LEMON-SHERRY PUDDING

Serves 6.   Calories per serving: 90.

2 Tbs. sifted flour	1 Tbs. Sucaryl
2 Tbs. sugar	3 Tbs. sherry
½ tsp. salt	2 Tbs. lemon juice
½ tsp. cinnamon	1 cup skim milk
2 eggs	2 egg whites, stiffly beaten
1 egg yolk	

☞ Sift the flour, sugar, salt, and cinnamon into a bowl. Beat the eggs, egg yolk, Sucaryl, sherry, and lemon juice together. Gradually add the dry ingredients, beating well. Stir in the milk and then fold in the egg whites. Turn into a 1½-quart casserole. Place in a shallow pan of hot water. Bake 30 minutes. Serve cold.

TOTAL CALORIES FOR THE DAY: 646, INCLUDING
59 OF SNACKS

63 *Breakfast*	109 *Lunch*	415 *Dinner*
28 ½ cup Mott's Apple Grape juice	100 Egg Florentine (page 58)	190 Bouillabaisse*
	9 Orange D-Zerta	100 2 slices French bread
35 1 slice gluten toast	Tea with lemon	75 Caesar salad (page 119)
Black coffee	Midafternoon drink	50 ½ grapefruit
1 Midmorning snack		Black coffee
		58 6 oz. skim milk

BOUILLABAISSE

Serves 6.   Calories per serving: 190.

2 Tbs. olive oil	1 tsp. saffron
3 onions, chopped fine	1 lb. assorted sliced fish
2 cloves garlic	(perch, pike, haddock)
5 tomatoes, chopped fine, or 2	5 cups boiling water
cups canned	2 lobsters (1 lb. each) cut up
1 bay leaf	6 shrimp, shelled and cleaned
1 tsp. salt	6 clams or mussels in the shell
½ tsp. pepper	1 cup dry white wine

☞ Heat the oil in a large casserole or Dutch oven. Sauté the onions and garlic for 5 minutes. Add the tomatoes. Cook 10 minutes. Add the bay leaf, salt, pepper, saffron, fish, and boiling water. Cook over low heat for 10 minutes. Carefully place the lobster in the casserole. Cook 10 minutes. Add the shrimp, clams, and wine. Cook 7 minutes. Taste for seasoning. Place piece of fish, lobster, shrimp, and clams in deep soup plate. Pour the soup over it. Serve with French bread.

TOTAL CALORIES FOR THE DAY: 628, INCLUDING
1 OF SNACKS

30	*Breakfast*	210	*Lunch*	387	*Dinner*
30	½ cantaloupe Black coffee	60	1 artichoke vinaigrette (page 18)	250	4 oz. filet of beef (tour-nedos)*
1	Midmorning drink	50	½ oz. Camem-bert with	12	Green beans
		100	Fresh Bosc pear	30	Broiled tomato
			Tea with lemon	20	Endive salad
				75	Macedoine of fresh fruit*
			Midafternoon drink		Black coffee
					Have some low-calorie root beer tonight

TOURNEDOS OF BEEF

☞ We took an "Hysterical Tour" of Denmark one summer
when several of the children were quite young and every night
they had the same thing for dinner—"tornados," as in Kansas.
The Danish beef was wonderful and most inexpensive. Just
take a 4-ounce piece of filet of beef and broil to the desired
degree of doneness.

MACEDOINE OF FRESH FRUIT

☞ Put whatever kind of fresh fruit you have together and
put on 1 teaspoon Kirsch.

TOTAL CALORIES FOR THE DAY: 570, INCLUDING
58 OF SNACKS

122	*Breakfast*	175	*Lunch*	215	*Dinner*
50	½ cup orange juice	10	Consommé	120	Coquilles St. Jacques*
50	½ cup Cream of Wheat	70	Scrambled egg in	25	Kohlrabi
22	2 oz. skim milk Black coffee	30	Tomato cup* with 2 anchovies on top	30	Grated carrot salad* in lettuce cup
	Midmorning drink	65	Baked apple Tea with lemon	40	Lemon sherbet with creme de menthe*
			Midafternoon tea	22	2 oz. skim milk Black coffee
				58	6 oz. skim milk at bedtime

COQUILLES ST. JACQUES NO. 1

Serves 4. Calories per serving: 120.

24 scallops
1 cup tomato juice
½ cup dry white wine
1 Tbs. lemon juice
2 or 3 drops Worcestershire sauce

2 or 3 drops Tabasco
1 Tbs. parsley, chopped
Salt, pepper, celery salt, garlic salt, onion salt
1 oz. brandy

☞ In a small saucepan combine tomato juice, wine, lemon juice, Worcestershire sauce, Tabasco, chopped parsley, and seasonings to taste. When liquid is hot, add scallops and simmer for 10 minutes. Carefully drain off liquid and reserve.

Pour heated brandy into saucepan and light. Return liquid to saucepan and bring to boiling point. Serve in warm plates or scallop shells.

GRATED CARROT SALAD

☞ Mix grated carrots with low-calorie mayonnaise and plop into a lettuce leaf.

LEMON SHERBET WITH CRÈME DE MENTHE

Serves 4. Calories per serving: 40.

¾ cup water	⅛ cup powdered skim milk
1 tsp. Sucaryl	Drop or two of yellow food
¼ cup lemon juice	coloring
¼ cup orange juice	4 tsp. creme de menthe
½ tsp. lemon rind	

☞ Combine water, Sucaryl, lemon juice, orange juice and grated rind. Strain. Add dry milk and food coloring; blend well. Place in freezer tray for 45 minutes. Turn into chilled bowl and beat with chilled electric beater until frothy. Return to freezer until almost set. Beat again with chilled equipment and freeze until firm enough to spoon out. Serve in sherbet glasses with 1 teaspoon of creme de menthe on each serving.

TOTAL CALORIES FOR THE DAY: 679, INCLUDING
59 OF SNACKS

87	*Breakfast*	238	*Lunch*	295	*Dinner*
50	½ grapefruit	150	Chicken livers,	135	Ham soufflé*
35	1 slice gluten		bacon,	47	½ cup parsnips
	toast with	30	and cherry	50	Orange and red
2	Diet jam		tomatoes *en*		onion salad*
	Black coffee		*brochette**	63	Mocha pot de
		15	Watercress		creme*
1	Midmorning		salad		Black coffee
	drink	43	½ cup diet		
			pears	58	6 oz. skim milk
			Tea with lemon		at bedtime
			Midafternoon		
			bouillon		

CHICKEN LIVERS AND BACON
EN BROCHETTE

2 chicken livers per person: 180 calories.

☞ Cut the chicken livers into about 3 pieces each. Thread
on the skewers, alternating with a square of bacon, 1 piece per
person, and cherry tomatoes. Brush with diet Italian salad
dressing and broil until done.

HAM SOUFFLÉ

Serves 3.   Calories per serving: 135.

☞ Use the recipe on page 25, but substitute ground ham
(8 ounces) for the cheese and add 1 teaspoon mustard.

ORANGE AND RED ONION SALAD

☞ Use ½ navel orange per serving, peeled and cut through in circles. Use as many red onion rings as you want and put diet Italian dressing on.

MOCHA POT DE CRÈME

☞ Use the recipe on page 52. This is a great-tasting dessert.

SUMMER MENUS

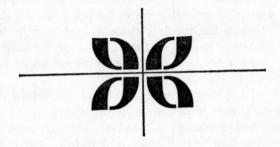

Summer is an ideal time to lose weight because when it is hot you really don't feel like eating or cooking. It is also easier to exercise. Swimming, golf, tennis, and gardening give you a chance to be outdoors without its seeming like a chore. There are fewer formal parties. Barbecues and picnics lend themselves to lighter-calorie menus; a cold buffet does not harbor as many pitfalls as a six-course sitdown dinner. It is easier to prepare a jellied salad as a main course dish in the cool hours of early morning, and a beautiful dish of fresh raspberries is more appealing to me than any chocolate mousse or seven-layer cake. Veal is a marvelous meat for the weight-conscious; it has considerably fewer calories than beef. In many parts of the country salmon is the traditional feast for the Fourth of July. Soft-shell crabs are in season, and of course lobsters and clams.

The luau is now in style in all the other forty-nine states as well as in Hawaii. One of the most spectacular desserts at a pool party is a watermelon basket filled with every kind of fresh fruit in the market, surrounded by half-pineapples which have been sliced lengthwise, including the leaves, scooped out, and filled with strawberries.

Deep-red juicy tomatoes are low in calories. Sliced about an inch thick, sprinkled with basil or oregano and a good wine vinegar, then spiced with freshly ground black pepper, they are eye- and mouth-appealing. Most people who have never eaten them, think currants are good only for jelly, but raspberries and red currants in equal amounts, sweetened with Sucaryl, and served icy cold, makes a modern version of my grandmother's favorite summer dessert. Blackberries, local strawberries, melons, and pears are all welcome additions to the dieter's board. Although freezing is a modern food miracle, in the summer we return to shelling fresh peas, snapping beans, and washing spinach because there is really no substitute for the indefinable delight of fresh food.

The salad bowl is the mainstay of any determined dieter. Summer is the time to find the most variety among the bulky, vitamin-packed greens that will peel off those ugly pounds and put more zip into your life. Be adventurous. Put different things in your salads. Have you ever tried a raw mushroom salad? It is delightful. Mushrooms are extremely low in calories and one of the most versatile of all vegetables. They can be stuffed, put under meats and other foods, sliced and put on top of foods of many kinds, hidden in an omelet, obscured in a salad, used to fill up that hungry void without filling out those unsightly bulges. Blueberries, the big fat ones, sprinkled over a fruit salad give an accent to both taste and vision that is hard to resist.

If you find yourself longing for a blueberry pie, sweeten the berries with Sucaryl and gently stew them till they burst (forget about the piecrust—that way lies disaster) and call it a blueberry compote.

If you are going to stay on the diet you must learn to tempt yourself with all the wonderful low-calorie foods so abundantly present in this great country.

Summer Menus

Main dishes for dinner

❧ WEEK 1 ❧

Baked filet of sole
Filet of beef
Chicken cacciatore
Tongue in aspic
Liver braised with vegetables
Escalope de veau
Asparagus and shrimp salad

❧ WEEK 2 ❧

Veal ragout
Soft-shelled crab
Lamb and eggplant casserole
Shrimp teriyaki
Far Eastern chicken
Fish mousse
Hot ham and banana rolls

❧ WEEK 3 ❧

Liver with brown sauce
Chicken in tomato aspic ring

Baked stuffed eggplant
Ducklings in orange mold
Peppers stuffed with wild rice
Liver rolls creole
Molded chicken and pineapple salad

WEEK 4

Salmon ring with peas
Veal chop violette
Coquilles St. Jacques
Beefsteak tartare
Beef tongue jardinière
Cold filet of beef
Jellied beef à la mode

WEEK 5

Ham mousse
Jellied salmon rings
Smothered calves' liver
Chicken breasts Grand Marnier
California veal rolls
Shrimp in aspic
Skewered swordfish

WEEK 6

London broil
Baked stuffed lobster
Broiled chicken
Beef tenderloin en ficelle
Salmon steak
Muslim kabobs
Asparagus chicken salad

TOTAL CALORIES FOR THE DAY: 618, INCLUDING
59 OF SNACKS

65	*Breakfast*	145	*Lunch*	349	*Dinner*
30	Sliced fresh peach	15	Cold chicken consommé	204	Baked filet of sole*
35	1 slice gluten toast	100	Crabmeat salad	30	Tomatoes vinaigrette*
	Black coffee	30	Small bunch seedless grapes	40	Spinach in red wine*
1	Midmorning low-calorie drink		Iced tea	75	Cold lemon soufflé*
			Midafternoon drink		Black coffee
				58	6 oz. skim milk at bedtime

BAKED FILET OF SOLE

Serves 3.   Calories per serving: 204.

1 lb. filet of sole
1 can diet cream of mushroom
   soup

2 Tbs. dry white wine
Few grains cayenne

☞ Preheat oven to 350 degrees. Heat and stir until smooth condensed mushroom soup mixed with white wine and cayenne. Pour this sauce over the fish and bake uncovered for 10 minutes.

[*continued*]

TOMATOES VINAIGRETTE

Serves 3.   Calories per serving: 30.

1 can whole peeled deluxe tomatoes	Salt and pepper
2 Tbs. vinegar	Dried dill weed
¼ tsp. Sucaryl	Onion rings

☞ Carefully remove the tomatoes from the can so they keep their shape. Mix the vinegar and Sucaryl together, and spoon over the tomatoes. Sprinkle with salt and pepper, dill weed, and garnish with onion rings.

SPINACH IN RED WINE

Serves 3.   Calories per serving: 40.

1 Tbs. cooking oil	¼ cup red wine
1 small can mushrooms, drained	1 pkg. chopped frozen spinach, cooked and drained
1 clove garlic, pressed	
½ tsp. prepared mustard	Salt and pepper

☞ Heat the oil in the Teflon pan and sauté the mushrooms and garlic for 5 minutes. Add the mustard and wine; cover and simmer for 8 minutes. Stir in the cooked spinach. New taste thrill.

COLD LEMON SOUFFLÉ

Serves 6.   Calories per serving: 75.

1 envelope gelatin	4 eggs
¼ cup cold water	2 Tbs. Sucaryl
1 tsp. lemon rind, grated	½ tsp. salt
½ cup lemon juice	1 cup whipped topping

☞ Sprinkle the gelatin over the cold water to soften. Grate enough lemon rind to measure 1 teaspoon and extract the lemon juice. Separate the eggs. Mix yolks with lemon juice and 1 tablespoon Sucaryl and salt in top of double boiler. Cook over boiling water, stirring constantly, until slightly thick and custardy. Stir in gelatin and lemon rind. Cool. Beat egg whites until they hold a shape. Now pile cream (whipped topping) on top of egg whites and stir into lemon mixture very gently. Pour into 2-quart soufflé dish and chill 2 to 3 hours until firm but spongy. Heavenly.

TOTAL CALORIES FOR THE DAY: 598, INCLUDING 29 OF SNACKS

	Breakfast		*Lunch*		*Dinner*
47		185		307	
12	½ cup diet cranberry juice	125	Spanish omelet (page 128) garnished with	250	4 oz. filet of beef, broiled, roasted, or cold leftover
35	1 slice gluten toast	10	Watercress	25	Braised celery (page 38)
	Black coffee	50	¼ honeydew melon	25	Tiny whole baby carrots
1	Midmorning low-calorie drink		Iced tea	7	Lime chiffon (page 23)
			Midafternoon bouillon		Black coffee
				58	6 oz. skim milk at bedtime

The filet of beef can be any way you want it. If it is hot, have it cold. If it is a cool night, have it hot. If you are having company, have it roasted. Save the tails to make Steak Tartare for lunch some day soon. Have it Chateaubriand. Go out to dinner. Any self-respecting French restaurant has gorgeous *Filet de Boeuf.*

TOTAL CALORIES FOR THE DAY: 603, INCLUDING
59 OF SNACKS

25	*Breakfast*	205	*Lunch*	314	*Dinner*
25	½ cup V-8 juice Black coffee	150	Cold sliced tongue with Dijon	130	Chicken cacciatore*
1	Midmorning low-calorie drink		mustard	109	½ cup cooked spaghetti
		25	1 sliced fresh tomato	15	Mixed green salad
		30	1 fresh peach Iced tea	60	D-Zerta butterscotch pudding Black coffee
			Midafternoon tea		
				58	6 oz. skim milk at bedtime

CHICKEN CACCIATORE

Serves 4. Calories per serving: 130.

4 lb. chicken	¾ cup chicken stock
2 Tbs. shallots, chopped	½ bay leaf
1 garlic clove, minced	⅛ tsp. thyme
¼ cup Italian tomato paste	⅛ tsp. marjoram
½ cup dry white wine	1 cup sliced mushrooms
1 tsp. salt	2 Tbs. brandy
¼ tsp. white pepper	

☞ Brown the chicken in the Teflon pan. Add the rest of the ingredients, cover and simmer for 1 hour or until tender. Serve with ½ cup boiled spaghetti.

TOTAL CALORIES FOR THE DAY: 639, INCLUDING
59 OF SNACKS

110	*Breakfast*	104	*Lunch*	366	*Dinner*
75	Scrambled egg	50	½ cup skim-	160	Tongue in
35	1 slice gluten		milk cottage		aspic*
	toast		cheese with	75	1 deviled egg
	Black coffee	35	Chopped	10	Lettuce
1	Midmorning		radishes,	20	Asparagus
	low-calorie		green		vinaigrette
	drink		pepper, and	101	Pineapple
			onion in a		sherbet in
			tomato cup		orange cup*
		10	1 Diet-10		Black coffee
			cracker	58	6 oz. skim milk
		9	Strawberry		at bedtime
			D-Zerta		
			Iced tea		
			Midafternoon tea		

TONGUE IN ASPIC

Serves 8.   Calories in 3 slices: 160.

1 smoked beef tongue, cooked	½ cup sweet-sour pickles, chopped
1½ Tbs. gelatin	1 cup celery, chopped
½ cup cold beef stock	½ cup green peppers, chopped
2½ cups boiling beef stock	**Cold cooked carrots**
Juice of 2 lemons	**Cold cooked beets**
3 drops Sucaryl	**Canned mushrooms**
Few drops Gravy Master	[*continued*]
1 tsp. Worcestershire sauce	

☞ Cool the tongue in the stock, then trim nicely. Make the aspic as follows: Soak 1½ tablespoons gelatin in ½ cup cold beef stock. Dissolve in 2½ cups boiling stock to which has been added the lemon juice, Sucaryl, and Gravy Master. Chill the aspic and when it has nearly set, add the other ingredients. Have at hand a mold that has been dipped in cold water. Place a small amount of aspic in the bottom and make a design with the cooked vegetables. When this has set, place the tongue in the mold and pour the remaining aspic over it. When well chilled, unmold onto a serving platter and garnish with deviled eggs (diet style for those who must), parsley, lemon slices, and lettuce. This can be a big production number for a summer buffet.

PINEAPPLE SHERBET IN ORANGE CUPS

Serves 6. Calories per serving: 101.

2 cups buttermilk	1 Tbs. Sucaryl
1 can frozen concentrated	6 small oranges
pineapple juice	6 whole strawberries

☞ Combine buttermilk and pineapple juice with Sucaryl. Beat until well blended. Pour into an ice-cube tray and freeze until firm almost to the middle. Spoon into a chilled bowl. Beat quickly until fluffy smooth. Return to tray and freeze 2 or 3 hours or until firm. Separate the peeled oranges slightly and place in a dessert dish. Scoop sherbet into the middle and garnish each with a strawberry.

TOTAL CALORIES FOR THE DAY: 615, INCLUDING
59 OF SNACKS

37 Breakfast	191 Lunch	328 Dinner
37 2 oz. cranberry juice, 2 oz. orange juice	116 Artichoke soufflé*	200 Liver braised with vege- tables*
Black coffee	15 Watercress and radishes	68 1 ear of fresh corn!!
1 Midmorning low-calorie drink	60 3 fresh apricots Iced tea	15 Mixed green salad
	Midafternoon tea	45 Apple whip* Black coffee
		58 6 oz. skim milk at bedtime

ARTICHOKE SOUFFLÉ

Serves 6. Calories per serving: 116.

6 artichokes	Salt and pepper
Lemon juice	4 eggs, separated
1½ Tbs. flour	2 extra egg whites
½ cup hot skim milk	

☞ Boil the artichokes for 40 minutes or until they are
tender. Scrape the tender parts from the base of each leaf and
add the bases of the artichokes from which the chokes have
been removed. Mash together well, sprinkle with lemon juice
to keep the pulp from darkening, and force through a strainer.
Put this purée into a saucepan, stir in 1½ tablespoons flour,
and add gradually ½ cup hot milk. Cook the mixture for 2 or

[continued]

3 minutes, stirring. Remove it from the fire and add salt and pepper and 1 tablespoon of lemon juice. Beat the 6 egg whites until stiff and fold them into the yolk mixture. Pour the mixture into a lightly greased 2-quart soufflé mold and bake it in a 475-degree oven for 10 minutes or until it rises. Lower the heat to 275 degrees and cook for another 15 minutes. Serve at once.

LIVER BRAISED WITH VEGETABLES

Serves 6. Calories per serving: 200.

1½ lbs. calves' liver
1 Tbs. seasoned flour
1 Tbs. bacon drippings
2 carrots, diced
6 small onions

2 green peppers, seeded and chopped
1 cup celery, sliced
1 cup boiling water or stock

☞ Cut liver into 1-inch slices. Dust with flour. Brown the liver in the fat in the Teflon pan. Combine and heap the diced vegetables on the liver. Add to the pan 1 cup boiling water or stock; cover and simmer until the liver is tender, about 15 minutes.

APPLE WHIP

Serves 6. Calories per serving: 45.

5 egg whites
1 tsp. Sucaryl
3 Delicious apples

Nutmeg
Cinnamon

☞ Beat egg whites until stiff. Beat in Sucaryl. Core and peel the apples. Grate the apples into acidulated water (1 teaspoon lemon juice to each cup of water) to cover, stirring often to keep the apples from discoloring. Drain apples thoroughly. Fold into the beaten egg whites. Sprinkle with nutmeg and cinnamon.

TOTAL CALORIES FOR THE DAY: 607, INCLUDING
59 OF SNACKS

37	*Breakfast*	120	*Lunch*	391	*Dinner*
35	1 slice gluten	15	Cold consommé	319	Escalope de
	toast with	75	Radish and raw		veau*
2	Diet marmalade		spinach	12	Green beans
	Black coffee		salad*	15	Mixed green
		30	1 fresh peach		salad
1	Midmorning		Iced tea	45	Blancmange*
	drink				Black coffee
			Midafternoon		
			tea	58	6 oz. skim milk
					at bedtime

RADISH AND RAW SPINACH SALAD

Serves 3.   Calories per serving: 75.

Small bunch radishes	Freshly ground black pepper
4 cups small fresh spinach	Lemon juice
leaves	1 finely chopped onion
3 slices crisp bacon	

☞ Crisp the bacon in the Teflon pan. Pour off the fat and
drain the bacon. Into the unwiped pan, put the finely chopped
onion and sauté until limp. Add the juice of 2 lemons. Slice
the radishes thin, wash the spinach leaves and dry well.
Crumble the bacon on top after you have poured the mixture
from the pan and tossed the salad well.

[continued]

ESCALOPE DE VEAU

Serves 6.   Calories per serving: 319.

6 slices veal, cut very thin	½ cup mushrooms
(1 lb. altogether)	Salt and pepper
2 Tbs. butter	6 tsps. liver pâté
½ cup cooked rice	6 tsps. brandy
½ cup white onions	Parmesan cheese

☞ Pound the veal until each piece is about 3 by 3 inches. Sauté the pieces in the butter until they are just barely frizzled on both sides. Now make what is called a soubise. Mix the rice, onions, and mushrooms well and grind in a food chopper. Season well with salt and pepper. Place 1 teaspoon liver pâté (Sell's will be fine) on each escalope. Press firmly over this ⅙ of the soubise. Sprinkle each escalope with 1 teaspoon of brandy and dust with Parmesan cheese. Place the escalopes on an ovenproof platter and bake for about 15 minutes in a 350-degree oven or until the cheese is golden. This whole thing can be prepared ahead of time and popped into the oven for the final 15 minutes.

TOTAL CALORIES FOR THE DAY: 601, INCLUDING 59 OF SNACKS

155	*Breakfast*	180	*Lunch*	207	*Dinner*
50	1 slice crisp bacon	100	Broiled calves' liver	55	Cream of cucumber soup*
70	1 poached egg on	20	Broccoli vinaigrette	112	Asparagus and shrimp salad*
35	1 slice gluten toast	60	D-Zerta chocolate pudding	40	Rhubarb compote*
	Black coffee		Iced tea		Black coffee
1	Midmorning drink		Midafternoon drink		
				58	6 oz. skim milk at bedtime

COLD CREAM OF CUCUMBER SOUP

Serves 6.   Calories per serving: 55.

2 cucumbers, pared and sliced	1 Tbs. cornstarch
1 onion, chopped	3 Tbs. cold water
4 cups chicken broth, fat-free	1 cup skim milk
¼ tsp. white pepper	1 Tbs. dill, finely chopped
1 bay leaf	

☞ Combine the cucumber, onion, chicken broth, pepper, and bay leaf in a saucepan. Bring to a boil and cook over low heat 20 minutes. Discard the bay leaf. Purée in the blender. Return to the saucepan. Mix the cornstarch and water until smooth and stir it into the soup. Cook over low heat, stirring

[*continued*]

constantly until the boiling point. Continue to simmer for 5 minutes. Add the milk; taste for seasoning and chill. Serve in chilled bowls, sprinkled with dill.

ASPARAGUS AND SHRIMP SALAD

Serves 6.   Calories per serving: 112.

1 lb. asparagus	6 artichoke bottoms (canned)
¾ lb. shrimp	Parsley
3 Tbs. diet mayonnaise	Diet Italian dressing
Juice of 1 lemon	1 hard-cooked egg, sieved

☞ Cook 1 pound of asparagus. Reserve 6 of the best stalks and cut the rest into 1-inch pieces. Cook, shell, and devein ¾ pound of fresh shrimp. Reserve 6 of them and dice the rest. Toss the cut-up asparagus and diced shrimp together with the mayonnaise which has been thinned with the lemon juice. Chill well in the refrigerator. Marinate 6 artichoke bottoms in the Italian dressing. Just before serving, place the salad in a bowl and sprinkle with the sieved hard-boiled egg and arrange the asparagus like the spokes of a wheel on top. Drain the artichoke bottoms and garnish each one with a dab of mayonnaise, 1 whole shrimp, and a sprig of parsley. Arrange them around the edge of the salad. Serve immediately.

RHUBARB COMPOTE

Serves 6.   Calories per serving: 40.

2 lbs. rhubarb	1 Tbs. Sucaryl
2 Tbs. sugar	1 tsp. vanilla extract

☞ Wash the rhubarb and cut into 1-inch pieces. Combine in saucepan with the sugar and Sucaryl. Cook over low heat 10 minutes, stirring frequently. Remove from the heat and add the vanilla. Chill.

TOTAL CALORIES FOR THE DAY: 594, INCLUDING
59 OF SNACKS

	Breakfast		Lunch		Dinner
12	*Breakfast*	105	*Lunch*	418	*Dinner*
12	½ cup diet cranberry juice Black coffee	15	Cold jellied chicken consommé	310	Veal ragoût*
		40	Asparagus salad	57	Mashed carrot ring* filled with
1	Midmorning drink	50	½ cantaloupe Iced tea	27	1 cup fresh peas
			Midafternoon tea	15	Mixed green salad
				9	Orange D-Zerta Black coffee
				58	6 oz. skim milk at bedtime

VEAL RAGOÛT

Serves 6.   Calories per serving: 310.

1½ lbs. boneless veal cut in 2-inch cubes	1½ cups boiling water
1 Tbs. butter	2 carrots, sliced
1 clove of garlic, pressed	3 stalks celery, sliced
1 Tbs. flour	2 potatoes, peeled and cubed
1½ tsps. salt	2 sprigs parsley
¼ tsp. pepper	1 cup shelled green peas
	½ tsp. marjoram

☞ Melt the butter in a Dutch oven. Sauté the veal until browned on all sides. Sprinkle with the flour, salt, and pepper, then add the water, stirring constantly until it reaches the
[*continued*]

boiling point. Cover and cook over low heat for 1¼ hours. Add the carrots, celery, parsley, peas, marjoram, and a little more water if necessary. Cover and cook over low heat for 30 minutes. Taste for seasoning. Skim off any fat; also blot the top with a paper towel.

MASHED CARROT RING

Serves 4.   Calories per serving: 57.

2 bunches young carrots	1 Tbs. chives, chopped
1 Tbs. butter	Dash of cloves
Salt and pepper	1 egg yolk

☞ Cook the carrots unpeeled. Cool and skin. Use a blender, put them through a ricer, or mash with a potato masher. Beat in the butter, salt, pepper, chives, and cloves. Beat in 1 egg yolk. Place in slightly oiled ring mold and heat over hot water in a 350-degree oven for 20 or 30 minutes. Invert the mold onto a serving plate and fill center with 1 cup of fresh green peas.

TOTAL CALORIES FOR THE DAY: 712, INCLUDING
59 OF SNACKS

72 *Breakfast*	158 *Lunch*	423 *Dinner*
50 ½ cup Puffed Wheat	40 Chilled tomato bouillon*	321 Broiled soft-shell crab*
22 2 oz. skim milk Black coffee	85 Open-face shrimp sandwich*	12 Broccoli
1 Midmorning drink	33 30 green seedless grapes Iced tea	35 Sliced tomatoes with oregano, salt, black pepper, and vinegar
	Midafternoon drink	55 Fresh fruit mélange Black coffee
		58 6 oz. skim milk at bedtime

CHILLED TOMATO BOUILLON

Serves 6.   Calories per serving: 40.

2 tsp. butter	½ tsp. oregano
1 onion, chopped	¼ tsp. celery salt
6 cups tomato juice	⅛ tsp. freshly ground black
1 bay leaf	pepper
½ cup celery with leaves, chopped	6 tsps. sour cream

☞ Melt the butter in a saucepan. Sauté the onion for 5 minutes, stirring frequently. Add the tomato juice, bay leaf, celery, oregano, celery salt, and pepper. Cook over low heat for

[continued]

15 minutes. Strain. Taste for seasoning. Serve well chilled with a spoonful of sour cream on top. Of course, if a front should come through and the weather turns cool, serve it hot.

OPEN-FACE SHRIMP SANDWICH

Serves 2.   Calories per serving: 85.

1 can Pacific Pearl canned shrimp	Lettuce
2 Tbs. diet mayonnaise	2 slices gluten bread

☞ Mix the shrimp with the mayonnaise. Put a lettuce leaf on 1 slice of gluten bread for each serving. Arrange the shrimps tidily around the bread, making a design (very Danish). Cut in 2 triangles. Have a pickle. Live a little.

BROILED SOFT-SHELL CRABS

Calories per 8-ounce serving: 231.

☞ Crabs vary in size. The tiny ones are best and, of course, you could have 2 or 3 of those. If the fish market only has large ones, then you may only have one. You're on your own. Melt 2 tablespoons butter and mix with 2 tablespoons lemon juice. Add a few grains cayenne and a few grains of black pepper. Dip the crabs in this, then into flour. Then shake them to remove as much flour as possible. Place them under a pre-heated broiler, 2 inches from the heat. Broil 5 minutes to a side or according to size.

FRESH FRUIT MÉLANGE

Serves 6.   Calories per serving: 55.

1 pineapple	1 sliced banana
1 cup sliced strawberries or	1 tsp. Sucaryl
whole raspberries	1 Tbs. Kirsch

☞ Cut pineapple in half and scoop out center. Combine pineapple chunks with other fruits and flavorings. Mix well and let marinate in the refrigerator for at least 30 minutes before serving. The pineapple shells may be used for serving—it does give that tropical touch.

TOTAL CALORIES FOR THE DAY: 635, INCLUDING 59 OF SNACKS

30	*Breakfast*	99	*Lunch*	447	*Dinner*
30	½ small cantaloupe	15	Cold consommé	332	Lamb and eggplant casserole*
	Black coffee	75	Fruit salad*		
1	Midmorning drink	9	Raspberry D-Zerta	15	Mixed green salad
			Iced tea	100	Lemon mousse*
			Midafternoon tea	58	6 oz. skim milk at bedtime

FRUIT SALAD

☞ This can be made at your discretion and with what you found at the fruit market. I just go wild in the summer over the fresh fruit. Have to hold myself in bounds, but it is so beautiful and tastes so heavenly, and if you use a little discretion, it isn't even bad for you. Take a ripe peach, peel it, and fill the center with fresh raspberries. Or fill honeydew melon with huge blueberries.

[continued]

LAMB AND EGGPLANT CASSEROLE

Serves 4.   Calories per serving: 332.

1 medium eggplant, pared and chopped fine	1 tsp. salt
2 cups ground lean lamb	¼ tsp. paprika
½ cup onion, chopped	½ tsp. curry powder
3 Tbs. parsley, chopped	1 cup canned tomatoes, chopped

☞ Preheat oven to 350 degrees. Grease a casserole lightly. Fill the casserole with all the ingredients, mixed well together. Bake, covered, for about ¾ hour, then remove the cover and let the top brown.

LEMON MOUSSE

Serves 4.   Calories per serving: 100.

1 envelope unflavored gelatin	Juice of 1½ lemons
2 Tbs. water	Grated skin of lemons
½ cup sweet white wine	4 eggs, separated
1 Tbs. Sucaryl	

☞ Soak the gelatin in the cold water. Mix the wine, Sucaryl, lemon juice, and grated rind together. Heat this in the top of a double boiler over hot water. Add the gelatin and stir until dissolved. Beat 4 egg yolks until they are very thick and light, then stir in the lemon-gelatin mixture. Beat the egg whites until stiff and fold them into the yolk mixture. Pour this mousse into a glass bowl and chill until it becomes firm but is still light and foamy.

TOTAL CALORIES FOR THE DAY: 601½,
INCLUDING 59 OF SNACKS

50	*Breakfast*	150½	*Lunch*	342	*Dinner*
50	1 slice honeydew melon	12½	Borscht (page 12)	193	Shrimp Teriyaki*
	Black coffee	85	Egg Romanoff*	100	½ cup rice
1	Midmorning drink	10	Radishes and watercress	12	Asparagus
		43	½ cup blueberries	37	Fresh strawberries
			Iced tea	58	6 oz. skim milk at bedtime
			Midafternoon drink		

EGG ROMANOFF

Calories per serving: 85.

1 hard-boiled egg
Russian dressing, made with

diet dressing, mayonnaise,
and sweet pickle relish

SHRIMP TERIYAKI

Serves 3. Calories per serving: 193.

1 lb. uncooked shrimp, shelled
and deveined
2 to 4 Tbs. Teriyaki

½ cup unsweetened pineapple
juice
2 Tbs. cooking oil

☞ Marinate shrimp in other ingredients for 15 minutes.
Drain; broil in a preheated broiler 3 or 4 minutes on each side.

TOTAL CALORIES FOR THE DAY: 620, INCLUDING
59 OF SNACKS

37 *Breakfast*	155 *Lunch*	369 *Dinner*
37 2 oz. diet cranberry juice, with 2 oz. orange juice	15 Cold consommé	200 Far Eastern chicken*
	120 Tuna fish salad*	100 ½ cup white rice
	20 1 fresh plum	45 Braised celery* (page 38)
Black coffee	Iced tea	
1 Midmorning low-calorie drink	Midafternoon drink	15 Mixed green salad
		9 Lemon D-Zerta
		58 6 oz. skim milk at bedtime

TUNA FISH SALAD

Serves 6. Calories per serving: 120.

1 can water-packed tuna fish
2 stalks celery, diced
2 tomatoes cut in wedges
1 green pepper, julienne
2 heads romaine, in bite-size pieces
1 bunch watercress
3 Tbs. diet mayonnaise

☞ Drain the tuna fish and break it into chunks. Combine with the celery, tomatoes, green pepper, lettuce, and watercress in large salad bowl. Add the dressing and mix gently.

FAR EASTERN CHICKEN

Serves 3.   Calories per serving: 200.

½ cup plain yogurt
½ tsp. garlic powder
1 frying chicken, cut up
1 onion, chopped fine
¾ tsp. salt

¼ tsp. powdered ginger
½ Tbs. curry powder
½ tsp. cornstarch
2 Tbs. butter

☞ Mix the yogurt and garlic powder in a bowl. Add the chicken and marinate for 2 hours, turning frequently to coat the chicken. Melt the butter in a casserole. Sauté the onions 10 minutes, stirring frequently. Sprinkle with the salt, ginger, curry, and cornstarch, mixing well. Drain the chicken. Save the marinade. Add the chicken to the casserole and brown lightly. Add the reserved marinade. Cover and cook over low heat 1½ hours or until chicken is tender.

TOTAL CALORIES FOR THE DAY: 596, INCLUDING
59 OF SNACKS

72	*Breakfast*	180	*Lunch*	285	*Dinner*
50	½ cup Puffed Wheat	115	Fresh tomato stuffed with crabmeat on watercress	100	Fish mousse*
22	2 oz. skim milk Black coffee			42	Harvard beets
				92	Stuffed baked potato*
1	Midmorning low-calorie drink	65	1 sliced fresh orange Iced tea	12	Cucumber salad
			Midafternoon bouillon	39	½ cup fresh raspberries
				58	6 oz. skim milk at bedtime

FISH MOUSSE

Serves 2.   Calories per serving: 100.

2 envelopes lemon flavor
   D-Zerta gelatin
8 oz. cold flaked cod or
   haddock

2 tsp. onion juice
2 tsp. low-calorie mayonnaise
2 tsp. lemon juice
1 tsp. salt

☞ Dissolve gelatin in 1 cup boiling water and chill until syrupy. Mix other ingredients together and fold into the chilled gelatin. Pour into 1-pint mold and chill until firm. To serve, turn out on chilled serving plate garnished with salad greens and radishes.

STUFFED BAKED POTATO

Serves 4.   Calories per serving: 92.

2 freshly baked medium potatoes	⅔ cup cottage cheese
⅓ cup skim milk	Salt, pepper, and paprika

☞ Cut the baked potatoes in half and carefully scoop out the potato. Mash well. Beat in the skim milk. Then add the cottage cheese and season well with salt and pepper. Beat well. Stuff the potato shells with this mixture and sprinkle with paprika. Return the potatoes to a hot (400-degree) oven and bake until the top is brown.

TOTAL CALORIES FOR THE DAY: 629, INCLUDING
59 OF SNACKS

110	*Breakfast*	161	*Lunch*	299	*Dinner*
75	Scrambled egg	102	Different	215	Hot ham and
35	1 slice gluten		Gazpacho*		banana rolls*
	toast	50	Small fruit	12	Turnip greens
	Black coffee		salad	15	Mixed green
		9	Orange D-Zerta		salad
1	Midmorning		Iced tea	57	Biscuit Tortoni
	low-calorie			58	6 oz. skim milk
	drink		Midafternoon		at bedtime
			tea		

DIFFERENT GAZPACHO

Serves 6.   Calories per serving: 102.

2 egg yolks, hard-boiled, finely chopped	1 quart tomato juice
2 Tbs. olive oil	1 green pepper, minced
1 onion, chopped fine	2 egg whites, hard-boiled, julienne
1 clove garlic, pressed	1 small cucumber, cut fine
Juice of 1 lemon	1 lemon, sliced thin
1½ tsps. Worcestershire sauce	2 pimentos, julienne
1 dash Tabasco	12 ice cubes
1 tsp. dry mustard	Salt and pepper to taste

☞ Blend the egg yolks and olive oil into a smooth paste in a bowl. Use a mortar and pestle if you have one. Mix together the chopped onion, garlic, lemon juice, Worcestershire sauce, Tabasco, dry mustard, and salt and pepper. Add to egg yolk mixture. Work in the tomato juice. Mix in a separate bowl the minced green pepper, egg whites, chopped cucumber, lemon slices, and pimento strips. Chill both mixtures for about 3 hours. To serve, divide the chopped vegetable mixture among 6 chilled soup bowls. Place 2 ice cubes in each bowl and pour in the liquid. Andalusian, somebody said.

HOT HAM AND BANANA ROLLS

Serves 4.   Calories per serving: 215.

4 thin slices boiled ham	1½ Tbs. butter
4 firm bananas	Prepared mustard

☞ Spread mustard lightly on each ham slice. Peel bananas and wrap each in prepared ham slice. Brush tips of bananas with melted butter. Place in a baking dish with remaining butter. Bake in a moderate oven (350 degrees) 30 minutes, or until tender.

BISCUIT TORTONI

Serves 4.   Calories per serving: 57.

2 Tbs. lemon juice	¼ tsp. almond extract
½ cup non-fat skim milk powder	2 tsp. Sucaryl
	2 vanilla wafers

☞ Place ½ cup cold water and lemon juice in a mixing bowl. Add milk powder and beat with electric beater until stiff. Add Sucaryl and almond extract. Beat in until thoroughly mixed. Pour mixture into 4 5-ounce custard cups. Sprinkle with finely crushed vanilla wafers. Freeze as quickly as possible and serve when just frozen.

TOTAL CALORIES FOR THE DAY: 579, INCLUDING
59 OF SNACKS

60	*Breakfast*	153	*Lunch*	307	*Dinner*
60	2 fresh plums	90	3 oz. crabmeat	222	Liver with
	Black coffee		on		brown sauce*
1	Midmorning	5	Lettuce	12	½ cup turnip
	drink	20	Carrot sticks		greens
		5	Celery stalk	15	½ cup
		43	½ cup		cauliflower
			blueberries	15	Coleslaw
			Iced tea	43	Diet pears
					Black coffee
			Midafternoon		
			tea	58	6 oz. skim milk
					at bedtime

LIVER WITH BROWN SAUCE

Serves 4.   Calories per serving: 222.

4 slices lean bacon	1½ Tbs. flour
1 lb. calf's liver	1 tsp. Worcestershire sauce
1½ cups hot beef stock	Salt

☞ Cook bacon in Teflon pan. Remove from fat. Drain most of the fat. Keep bacon warm. Cut liver in pieces and dredge in the flour. Brown quickly on each side in the frying pan. Place liver on a hot platter with the bacon. Blend flour with juices in the pan, add hot stock, stirring until sauce thickens. Add Worcestershire sauce and salt. Pour sauce over liver and serve.

TOTAL CALORIES FOR THE DAY: 625, INCLUDING
59 OF SNACKS

72	*Breakfast*	208	*Lunch*	286	*Dinner*
50	1 cup Puffed Wheat (not sugar-coated)	130	Curried lobster and egg casserole*	166	Chicken in tomato aspic ring*
		15	Mixed green salad	30	Tomato wedges
22	2 oz. skim milk Black coffee			19	Stuffed celery stick*
		63	Mocha Pot de Crème (page 52)	71	Luau melon bowls*
1	Midmorning drink		Iced tea		Black coffee
			Midafternoon tea	58	6 oz. skim milk at bedtime

CURRIED LOBSTER AND
EGG CASSEROLE

Serves 6.   Calories per serving: 130.

1	medium onion, minced	Salt and pepper
¼	cup green pepper, minced	1½ cups cooked lobster, diced
1	cup fresh mushrooms, sliced	1 Tbs. parsley, minced
1	can diet mushroom soup	4 hard-cooked eggs, peeled
1½	tsp. curry powder	and quartered

☞ Simmer onion, green pepper, and mushrooms in 1 cup water for 15 minutes. Stir in the mushroom soup, curry powder, and salt and pepper to taste. Simmer, stirring, until smooth and thickened, about 5 minutes. Add lobster meat, parsley, eggs, and heat through. Serve in a casserole. You may add more curry powder if you like it hot.

[continued]

CHICKEN IN ASPIC

Serves 6.   Calories per serving: 166.

2 cups tomato juice
4 chicken bouillon cubes
1 bay leaf
4 peppercorns
4 whole cloves
Few sprigs parsley

2 Tbs. unflavored gelatin
2 tsp. sugar
Salt and pepper to taste
2 cups cubed cooked or canned
chicken

☞ Heat tomato juice with the bouillon cubes, bay leaf, spices, and parsley. Cover and simmer 10 minutes. Strain. Soften gelatin in ¼ cup cold water. Add tomato-juice mixture and stir until gelatin dissolves. Add sugar, salt, and pepper. Chill until syrupy. Fold in chicken. Pour into ring mold and chill until firm. To serve, unmold on crisp salad greens.

STUFFED CELERY STICKS NO. 1

Serves 6.   Calories per serving: 19.

⅓ cup low-calorie cottage
cheese
2 Tbs. low-calorie blue cheese
dressing

Garlic powder to taste
6 inner stalks of celery
Paprika

☞ Season the cottage cheese with the blue cheese dressing and garlic powder, salt and pepper. Stuff celery with mixture, sprinkle with paprika and serve.

LUAU MELON BOWLS

Serves 6 or more. Calories per serving: 71.   ■ *This is a spectacular dessert and should be perfect for a poolside party.*

1 medium honeydew melon

1 cantaloupe

½ fresh pineapple

2 oranges, sections

1 cup green grapes, halved

1 box fresh strawberries

1 box fresh raspberries

2 Tbs. lime juice

1 cup low-calorie ginger ale

Fresh mint leaves

☞ Cut a 1-inch slice from the side of each melon so it will sit flat. Scoop out seeds and carefully cut out with a melon baller. Save shells. Scallop edges of melons. Scoop out pineapple half, saving shell. Dice pineapple. Combine all the fruits and lime juice. Chill until serving. Place fruit shells on large tray. Fill with fruit to 1 inch from tops. Add ginger ale to fruit and garnish with mint sprigs.

TOTAL CALORIES FOR THE DAY: 609, INCLUDING
59 OF SNACKS

107	*Breakfast*	195	*Lunch*	248	*Dinner*
70	4 stewed prunes	110	Hasty Italian pizza*	15	Jellied consommé
35	1 slice gluten toast	15	Mixed green salad	181	Baked stuffed eggplant*
2	Diet wild strawberry jam	70	1 cup fresh raspberries	26	Coleslaw
	Black coffee		Iced tea	26	Spiced butter-scotch pudding*
1	Midmorning drink		Midafternoon tea		Black coffee
				58	6 oz. skim milk at bedtime

HASTY ITALIAN PIZZA

Serves 4.   Calories per serving: 110.

2 English muffins, split	¼ tsp. garlic, minced
4 slices fresh tomato	⅛ tsp. basil
¼ lb. ground steak	⅛ tsp. oregano
4 thin slices Mozzarella cheese	Pinch of crushed dried red peppers
½ Tbs. onion, chopped	Salt

 Lightly toast the split English muffins and place the 4 halves in a baking pan. Place a slice of tomato on top of each muffin slice and sprinkle with salt. Combine the ground beef, onion, garlic, and ¼ teaspoon salt. Spread this over the tomato. Add the cheese and sprinkle with the herbs. Bake in a hot oven (400 degrees) for 15 minutes.

BAKED STUFFED EGGPLANT

Serves 4. ¼ eggplant per person. Calories per serving: 181.

1 medium eggplant (1¼ lb.)	½ cup soft breadcrumbs
1 Tbs. onion, finely chopped	1 Tbs. chopped parsley
1 Tbs. green pepper, finely chopped	½ tsp. salt
	⅛ tsp. nutmeg
1 Tbs. butter	1 egg slightly beaten
½ lb. ground round steak	

☞ Cut eggplant in half lengthwise and cook in 2 quarts boiling water for 10 minutes. Pour off water and scoop out eggplant pulp, being sure not to break the skin. Leave the shell about ½ inch thick. Chop pulp and save. Sauté chopped onions and peppers in butter for about 5 minutes, until onions are limp and yellow. Add the meat and continue cooking until the meat loses its pink color. Stir constantly. Add the chopped eggplant pulp and breadcrumbs, parsley, salt, and nutmeg. Mix thoroughly. Remove from pan. When slightly cooled, stir in the lightly beaten egg. Fill the eggplant shells with this stuffing and place in a lightly greased baking pan. Bake in a moderate oven (350 degrees) for 45 minutes.

SPICED BUTTERSCOTCH PUDDING

Serves 2. Calories per serving: 26.

1 envelope D-Zerta butterscotch pudding	⅛ tsp. cloves
	⅛ tsp. allspice
½ Tbs. strong coffee	Rind of ¼ lemon, grated
⅛ tsp. cinnamon	

☞ Prepare pudding according to directions on package. When slightly cool, blend well with coffee and spices. Pour into 2 dessert glasses; chill until set. Top with grated lemon rind.

TOTAL CALORIES FOR THE DAY: 528, INCLUDING
59 OF SNACKS

100	*Breakfast*	143	*Lunch*	226	*Dinner*
25	½ cup tomato juice	100	Pineapple-tuna-celery salad*	140	Duckling in orange mold*
25	1 scrambled egg	34	2 Ry-Krisp		
50	1 slice crisp bacon	9	Orange D-Zerta Iced tea	28	Green beans and celery*
	Black coffee			58	Peach sherbet*
			Midafternoon drink		Black coffee
1	Midmorning drink				You have room for a cinnamon cookie (see page 219)
				58	6 oz. skim milk at bedtime

PINEAPPLE-TUNA-CELERY SALAD

Serves 6. Calories per serving: 100.

1 cup diet pineapple chunks
1 cup celery, diced
1 cup water-packed tuna, flaked

1 Tbs. lemon juice
3 Tbs. low-calorie mayonnaise
6 lettuce leaves
6 strips green pepper

☞ Combine the well-drained pineapple, celery, and tuna.
Add the lemon juice and mayonnaise. Mix well and chill.
Serve on a lettuce leaf garnished with a slice of green pepper.

DUCKLING IN ORANGE MOLD

Serves 6.   Calories per serving: 140.

> 2 envelopes orange flavor
>   D-Zerta
> 1½ cups boiling water
> 2 Tbs. lemon juice
> 2 cups cooled skinned lean
>   duck meat, diced

> 1 cup diet Mandarin orange
>   sections
> Watercress

☞ Place gelatin in a 2-quart mixing bowl. Add 1½ cups boiling water and lemon juice. Chill until syrupy. Stir in duck meat and orange sections. Place in a 1-quart ring mold. Chill until firm. Unmold on watercress.

GREEN BEANS AND CELERY

Serves 5.   Calories per serving: 28.

> 1½ cups sliced celery
> 1 tsp. salt
> 1⅓ cups boiling water

> 1 pkg. frozen cut green
>   beans

☞ Add celery and salt to boiling water in saucepan. Add frozen green beans and bring them to a boil again, separating the beans with a fork. Simmer for 10 minutes, or until beans are just tender. Drain and season to taste. Any leftovers can be used for cold string bean salad.

[*continued*]

PEACH SHERBET

Serves 6. Calories per serving: 58.

1 cup sliced fresh peaches	Salt
¼ cup lemon juice	1 egg white, stiffly beaten
Grated rind of a lemon	1 tsp. Sucaryl
2 cups buttermilk	

☞ Combine the peaches, which have been crushed or mashed with a fork, with the lemon juice and grated rind. Add buttermilk, salt, and Sucaryl. Pour into an ice-cube tray and set in freezing compartment of refrigerator. When the mixture is frozen almost solid, turn into a chilled bowl and whip very light. Add the beaten egg white. Return to freezer and freeze until set.

TOTAL CALORIES FOR THE DAY: 656, INCLUDING 59 OF SNACKS

	Breakfast		*Lunch*		*Dinner*
85		157		355	
50	½ cup orange juice	80	Seafood in aspic*	118	Peppers stuffed with wild rice*
35	1 slice gluten toast	77	Fresh pineapple	17	Simmered cucumbers*
	Black coffee		Iced tea	43	Carrot casserole
1	Midmorning drink		Midafternoon drink	177	Deep-dish apple pie*
					Black coffee
				58	6 oz. skim milk at bedtime

SEAFOOD IN ASPIC

Serves 4.   Calories per serving: 80.

1 bouillon cube
1 Tbs. unflavored gelatin
1 cup tomato juice
1 Tbs. lemon juice
½ tsp. A-1 sauce

½ tsp. salt
7-oz. can crabmeat
¼ cup green pepper, finely
 minced
Salad greens

☞ Dissolve bouillon cube in ½ cup boiling water. Soften gelatin in ¼ cup cold water, then dissolve over low heat. Combine dissolved bouillon cube, gelatin, tomato juice, lemon juice, A-1 sauce, and salt. Chill until beginning to thicken. Meanwhile, pick over the crabmeat, discarding any cartilage. Combine flaked crabmeat with the thickened gelatin mixture and stir in the green pepper. Pour into lightly oiled individual molds and chill until firm. Unmold onto crisp salad greens.

PEPPERS STUFFED WITH WILD RICE

Serves 3.   Calories per serving: 118.

1 cup cooked wild rice or
 brown rice if you're
 having budget problems
3 green peppers

¼ tsp. salt
¼ lb. chopped lean beef or
 ground leftover meat

☞ Mix rice, salt, and meat. Add a small amount of bouillon if rice is very dry. Fill peppers and place in baking dish. Surround peppers with a very small amount of hot water. Bake in 350-degree oven until peppers are tender. Wild rice is lower in calories than white rice. Costs more money, but much better for you.

[continued]

SIMMERED CUCUMBERS

Serves 3.   Calories per serving: 17.

2 medium cucumbers	2 Tbs. chopped parsley, dill,
⅓ cup tomato juice	or chives
¼ tsp. salt	

☞ Peel cucumbers if skin is tough. Slice lengthwise, 3 or 4 slices to each cucumber. Heat tomato juice, add cucumbers and salt. Cover and simmer until tender. Sprinkle generously with the herb.

DEEP-DISH APPLE PIE

Serves 3.   Calories per serving: 177.

2½ cups diced peeled apples	⅛ tsp. nutmeg
2 tsps. Sucaryl	⅛ tsp. cinnamon
1 tsp. Cream of Rice or	
tapioca	

PASTRY

⅓ cup cake flour	¼ tsp. salt
4 tsps. melted butter	1 Tbs. cold water

☞ Place apples in mixing bowl. Sprinkle in the cereal or tapioca, Sucaryl, nutmeg, and cinnamon. Mix together lightly. Divide apple mixture evenly among 3 shallow 3-inch casseroles. Place flour and salt in a mixing bowl. Add the melted butter. Add 1 tablespoon cold water. Mix thoroughly with a fork. Divide pastry into 3 portions. Roll out each on a lightly floured board to the size of the top of the casserole. Slash pastry circles to allow steam to escape. Top each pie with pastry circles. Bake in 400-degree oven about 30 minutes. Cool to room temperature and serve. Wow!

TOTAL CALORIES FOR THE DAY: 623, INCLUDING
59 OF SNACKS

110	*Breakfast*	65	*Lunch*	389	*Dinner*
75	1 egg omelet	20	Jellied	289	Liver rolls
35	1 slice gluten		consommé		creole*
	toast		½ clam juice	35	Cucumber and
	Black coffee		½ chicken		grapefruit
			broth		mold*
1	Midmorning		lemon juice	65	D-Zerta vanilla
	drink	15	Mixed green		pudding with
			salad		diet
		30	Stewed fresh		chocolate
			apricots		syrup
			Iced tea		Black coffee
			Midafternoon	58	6 oz. skim milk
			drink		at bedtime

LIVER ROLLS CREOLE

Serves 2.   Calories per serving: 289.

½ lb. calves' liver (2 slices)	1 bay leaf, crumbled
2 pork sausage links, halved	¼ tsp. salt
2 Tbs. onion, finely chopped	Dash of sugar
2 Tbs. green pepper, finely	Dash of Tabasco
chopped	½ cup celery, diced
1 10-oz. can whole tomatoes	

☞ Cut each piece of liver in half. There should be 4
pieces about 3 by 3 inches. Bring a small amount of water to
boil in a saucepan. Remove from heat. Dip liver pieces into
[*continued*]

hot water for a few seconds, just long enough to remove the red color from the surface of the liver. Place a sausage half on each piece of liver. Roll liver around sausage. Fasten with a toothpick. Place in small shallow baking dish. Combine onion, green pepper, tomatoes, bay leaf, salt, sugar, and Tabasco in a small saucepan. Bring to the boiling point. Reduce heat and simmer uncovered about 10 minutes. Add the celery and pour sauce over the liver rolls. Heat oven to 350 degrees. Bake 35 to 40 minutes, or until the liver is tender. Spoon sauce over the liver rolls several times during the baking period.

CUCUMBER AND GRAPEFRUIT MOLD

Serves 6.   Calories per serving: 35.

1 lb. can diet grapefruit sections	Few drops green food coloring
1 envelope plain gelatin	1 cup cucumber, peeled and diced
Few drops Sucaryl	
¼ tsp. salt	Watercress
1 Tbs. vinegar	

☞ Drain the syrup from the grapefruit sections and add enough water to make 1¾ cups liquid. Mix this liquid with the gelatin, sugar, and salt and stir over low heat until the gelatin is dissolved. Stir in the vinegar and a very little, green food coloring. Chill to the consistency of unbeaten egg whites. Fold in the cucumber and grapefruit, pour into a ring mold rinsed with cold water, and chill until firm. Serve on a chilled platter garnished with watercress.

TOTAL CALORIES FOR THE DAY: 541, INCLUDING 59 OF SNACKS

12	*Breakfast*	165	*Lunch*	305	*Dinner*
12	½ cup diet cranberry juice	45	Tomato stuffed with coleslaw	45	4 oz., Vichysoisse*
	Black coffee	120	1 slice watermelon, 4″ by 8″	185	Molded chicken and pineapple salad*
1	Midmorning drink		Iced tea	75	Angel cake (page 63) Black coffee
			Midafternoon drink	58	6 oz. skim milk at bedtime

VICHYSOISSE

☞ Use Campbell's frozen potato soup and follow directions, using skim milk instead of whole milk. Chop some chives on top. Nothing ever tasted so good.

MOLDED CHICKEN AND PINEAPPLE SALAD

Serves 4. Calories per serving: 185.

1 envelope plain gelatin	2 Tbs. lemon juice
1½ cups chicken stock	1½ cups cooked or canned chicken
½ tsp. salt	
¼ cup pineapple syrup (drained from can of fruit)	½ cup drained crushed diet pineapple
	½ cup celery, diced

[*continued*]

☞ Sprinkle the gelatin on half the chicken stock. Dissolve over low heat, stirring constantly. Remove from the heat and add the rest of the stock, salt, pineapple syrup, and lemon juice. Chill to the consistency of raw egg white. Fold in the chicken, pineapple, and celery. Turn into a small mold which . has been rinsed in cold water and chill until firm. Unmold onto a chilled plate and garnish with salad greens.

TOTAL CALORIES FOR THE DAY: 618, INCLUDING 59 OF SNACKS

	Breakfast		Lunch		Dinner
50	*Breakfast*	187	*Lunch*	322	*Dinner*
50	¼ honeydew melon	135	Chicken livers en brochette (page 105)	242	Salmon ring with peas*
	Black coffee			15	Cold broccoli vinaigrette
1	Midmorning drink	25	Stewed cucumbers	65	Frozen lemons à la Forum of the Twelve Caesars*
		27	½ cup fresh strawberries		
			Iced tea		Black coffee
			Midafternoon tea	58	6 oz. skim milk at bedtime

SALMON RING WITH PEAS

Serves 4. Calories per serving: 242.

2 eggs, lightly beaten	1 tsp. onion, grated
1 can diet cream of	Pepper
mushroom soup	Celery salt
4 saltines, crushed	16 oz. can salmon, drained,
¼ cup green pepper	picked over, and flaked
1 Tbs. parsley, minced	fine
1 Tbs. lemon juice	1 pkg. frozen peas

☞ Combine the eggs, half the soup, crumbs, green pepper, parsley, lemon juice, onion, dash of pepper, and a good pinch of celery salt. Stir into the salmon and spoon into a ring mold. Bake 40 to 50 minutes in a 350-degree oven and unmold onto a hot plate. Cook the peas in ½ cup boiling salted water, letting them simmer 2 minutes after the water comes to a boil again. Drain and mix gently with the rest of the mushroom soup which has been heated just to the boiling point. If it seems too thick, add a little skim milk. Pour the pea mixture into the center of the salmon ring. *Voilà!* That famous dish, salmon and peas. Leftover cooked salmon can be used instead of canned.

FROZEN LEMONS À LA
FORUM OF THE TWELVE CAESARS

Serves 6. Calories per serving: 65. ■ *Use the frozen lemonade sherbet recipe on page 262. 1 pint fills 6 lemon cups.*

☞ Cut the tops of 6 large lemons and hollow out. Mix ½ cup very finely diced mixed candied fruits with 1 pint of lemonade sherbet. Pile into the lemon shells and replace the tops of the lemons. Freeze at least 2 hours. Serve with a sprig of fresh mint tucked in the top.

TOTAL CALORIES FOR THE DAY: 617, INCLUDING
59 OF SNACKS

70	Breakfast	112	Lunch	376	Dinner
70	1 scrambled egg	42	Jellied beet	342	Veal chop
	Black coffee		and horse-		Violette*
1	Midmorning		radish salad*	15	½ cup mustard
	drink	15	6 cherries		greens
		25	1 small	10	Cucumber
			nectarine		salad
		30	1 small bunch	9	Raspberry
			seedless		D-Zerta
			grapes		Black coffee
			Iced tea		
				58	6 oz. skim milk
			Midafternoon		at bedtime
			broth		

JELLIED BEET AND
HORSERADISH SALAD

Serves 5. Calories per serving: 42.

2 Tbs. plain gelatin	1½ tsps. prepared horseradish
2 Tbs. cold water	Few drops Worcestershire
2 cups boiling water	sauce
½ cup lemon juice	¾ cup cabbage, finely
1 Tbs. Sucaryl	shredded
½ tsp. salt	¾ cup cooked beets, shredded
1 Tbs. vinegar	

☞ Sprinkle the gelatin over the cold water, then dissolve
in the boiling water. Combine with the lemon juice, Sucaryl,
salt, vinegar, horseradish, and Worcestershire sauce. Chill until

it begins to set. Stir the cabbage and beets into the partially set gelatin and pour into a mold. Chill until firm. Unmold on a bed of crisp greens and serve.

VEAL CHOP VIOLETTE

Serves 4. Calories per serving: 342.

1 Tbs. butter	½ cup veal or chicken stock
1 Tbs. onion, minced	½ cup dry white wine
2 Tbs. diced cooked ham or diced bacon	2 egg yolks, lightly beaten
Salt and pepper	1 Tbs. vinegar
4 veal chops, 1 inch thick	1 tsp. chopped parsley

☞ Heat the butter in the faithful Teflon pan and lightly brown the onion and ham or bacon. Season the chops and add them to the skillet, browning slowly on both sides until they are done. Remove them to a heated serving platter. Pour the fat from the pan and add the stock and wine. Turn up the heat and boil until the liquid is reduced by half. Mix a little of the hot liquid into the egg yolks and then pour them into the rest of the liquid. Stir constantly with a wire whisk until the sauce is smooth and thick. Add the vinegar and parsley when ready to serve. Stir in well and pour sauce over the warm chops.

TOTAL CALORIES FOR THE DAY: 636, INCLUDING
59 OF SNACKS

62 *Breakfast*	243 *Lunch*	272 *Dinner*
25 ½ cup tomato juice	45 Leeks vinaigrette*	112 Coquilles St. Jacques*
35 1 slice gluten bread	135 Open-face grilled cheese sandwich	70 Zucchini au bon goût*
2 Low-calorie jam		40 Artichoke hearts on watercress
Black coffee	63 D-Zerta butterscotch pudding	
1 Midmorning drink	Iced tea	50 Strawberries and pineapple on a pineapple shell
	Midafternoon tea	Black coffee
		58 6 oz. skim milk at bedtime

LEEKS VINAIGRETTE

Serves 4.   Calories per serving: 45.

4 leeks per person
1 tsp. prepared mustard
1 tsp. lemon juice

¼ cup Italian diet salad
dressing

☞ Trim the leeks and cut them lengthwise, but not to the root end. Wash thoroughly, making sure that all the sand is removed. Tie leeks together firmly and neatly. Drop into boiling salted water and simmer until tender, 15 or 20 minutes. Drain and chill. Mix the rest of the ingredients together. Mari-

nate the leeks in the dressing for an hour or more. Serve well
chilled, draped with a piece of pimento.

OPEN-FACED CHEESE SANDWICH

Serves 1. Calories per serving: 135.

1 slice gluten bread	Mustard
1 oz. Swiss or Ceddar cheese	

☞ Some sandwich, huh? May be broiled.

COQUILLES ST. JACQUES NO. 2

Serves 2. Calories per serving: 112.

½ lb. bay scallops	1 Tbs. parsley, chopped
White wine to cover	1 Tbs. shallots, chopped
1 Tbs. almonds, crushed	Salt
1 Tbs. chives, chopped	1 clove crushed garlic
1 Tbs. breadcrumbs	

☞ Poach the scallops in the white wine very gently. Remove
from wine and arrange in 2 scallop shells. Simmer the wine to
reduce by half. Stir in the rest of the ingredients and spread
this mixture over the scallops. Bake in the oven until top is
lightly browned.

[*continued*]

ZUCCHINI AU BON GOÛT

Serves 6.   Calories per serving: 70.

6 small whole zucchini, scrubbed and trimmed	diced and dried in slow oven
1½ cups peeled chopped tomatoes	Salt and freshly ground black pepper
¾ cup (2 slices) gluten bread	Grated Parmesan cheese

☞ Preheat oven to 450 degrees. Simmer the zucchini in a little water until barely tender, 8 to 10 minutes. Drain and, when cool, cut in half lengthwise. Scoop out seeds and invert the halves on paper towels to drain. Arrange the zucchini, cut side up, in a baking dish and fill the cavities with equal parts chopped tomatoes and croutons. Sprinkle with the salt, pepper, and cheese. Bake until heated through. Just before serving, brown under the broiler.

TOTAL CALORIES FOR THE DAY: 600, INCLUDING 59 OF SNACKS

	Breakfast		Lunch		Dinner
47	*Breakfast*	144	*Lunch*	350	*Dinner*
25	½ cup Puffed Rice	135	Chef's salad with 1 oz. tongue, julienne, ½ oz. Swiss cheese, greens	15	Cold consommé
22	2 oz. skim milk Black coffee			245	Beefsteak Tartare*
				30	Wilted Bibb lettuce
1	Midmorning drink	9	Lime D-Zerta Iced tea	60	Strawberry fluff*
					Black coffee
			Midafternoon tea	58	6 oz. skim milk at bedtime

BEEFSTEAK TARTARE

Serves 3.   Calories per serving: 245.

¾ lb. ground round steak, very lean	1 Tbs. capers
1 egg yolk	1 tsp. Worcestershire sauce
1 Tbs. onion, minced	Freshly ground black pepper
	Salt to taste

☞ If you have ever seen a *maître d'hotel* work up a Beef-steak Tartare, you know that it is quite a production. In the little bar at the Lausanne Palace in Lausanne, Switzerland, the headwaiter did a superb job. It is really easy. If you want to do this at the table, you make a mound of the beef and place the egg yolk in the center. The other things, capers and onions, are piled attractively on each side. You just mix and smooth and blend until this is done. Yes, you eat it raw.

STRAWBERRY FLUFF

Serves 4.   Calories per serving: 60.

2 cups crushed strawberries	¼ cup cold water
2 Tbs. Sucaryl	2 egg whites
1½ Tbs. plain gelatin	Juice of ½ lemon

☞ Stir 1 tablespoon of the Sucaryl into the crushed berries and cook them about 10 minutes over low heat. Sprinkle the gelatin over the ¼ cup cold water and add to the berries, stir-ring until dissolved. Chill. When the berry mixture begins to thicken, stir in the egg whites which have been sweetened with the rest of the Sucaryl and lemon juice and beaten until stiff. Pour into a mold which has been rinsed in cold water and chill until set. Unmold on a chilled plate and garnish with whole fresh strawberries.

TOTAL CALORIES FOR THE DAY: 601½, INCLUDING 59 OF SNACKS

70	*Breakfast*	131½	*Lunch*	341	*Dinner*
70	Boiled egg	12½	Cold borscht	205	Beef tongue
	Black coffee		(page 12)		jardinière*
1	Midmorning	46	Chinese	50	With
	drink		cabbage		vegetables
			bowl*	41	Pineapple
		73	Lemon		salad*
			tapioca	45	Lemon-Lime
			pudding*		royale*
			Iced tea		Black coffee
			Midafter-	58	6 oz. skim milk
			noon drink		at bedtime

CHINESE CABBAGE BOWL

Serves 4.   Calories per serving: 46.

6 cups Chinese cabbage,	½ cup green pepper, diced
shredded	¼ cup low-calorie blue cheese
1 cup celery, diced	dressing

☞ Combine cabbage, celery, and green pepper in salad bowl. Toss with blue cheese dressing. Chill at least an hour so the flavors blend.

LEMON TAPIOCA PUDDING

Serves 6.   Calories per serving: 73.

1 egg	½ tsp. vanilla
2¾ cups skim milk	Grated rind of 1 lemon
3 Tbs. quick-cooking tapioca	1 tsp. Sucaryl
⅛ tsp. salt	

☞ Beat egg with milk in saucepan. Stir in tapioca. Add salt. Let stand about 5 minutes. Cook, stirring constantly, 5 to 8 minutes or until mixture comes to a full rolling boil. Remove from heat. Stir in vanilla, lemon rind, and Sucaryl. Spoon into 6 sherbet glasses, dividing evenly. Chill.

BEEF TONGUE JARDINIÈRE

Serves many. Two ounces: 205 calories.

1 beef tongue	¼ cup peas
3 carrots	½ cup beans
2 turnips	6 small onions
3 stalks celery, cut	6 small tomatoes

☞ Boil the beef tongue 2 hours, skin and lay in a roasting pan on a layer of the diced vegetables listed. Pour around the tongue some of the water in which it was boiled. Cover and cook very slowly for 2 hours or longer, until tender. Remove tongue and, if today is terribly warm, let cool to room temperature. If cool enough, keep the tongue warm. Surround the tongue on the serving platter with vegetables. We like to slice the tongue before bringing to the table. If you are serving this cold, chill the vegetables.

[continued]

PINEAPPLE SALAD

Serves 6.   Calories per serving: 41.

6 cups salad greens, broken
1 can diet pack pineapple
   tidbits, drained
3 slices Bermuda onion, peeled
   and separated into rings

2 Tbs. low-calorie blue cheese
   dressing
2 Tbs. skim milk

☞ Place greens in large salad bowl. Top with the pine-apple chunks and onion rings. Mix the blue cheese dressing with the milk and drizzle over the salad. Toss lightly to mix.

LEMON-LIME ROYALE

Serves 6.   Calories per serving: 45.

2 envelopes low-calorie lemon
   gelatin (D-Zerta)
2 cups hot water

6 thin slices fresh lime
1 medium grapefruit
2 oranges

☞ Dissolve gelatin in hot water in a medium-size bowl. Chill until the consistency of unbeaten egg white. Spoon into 6 parfait glasses, dividing evenly. Carefully stand a lime slice in center of gelatin in each glass. Chill until firm. Pare grapefruit and oranges and section into a small bowl. When ready to serve, drain off the juice (may be saved for breakfast, 50 calories per 4-ounce glass). Spoon fruits on top of the gelatin.

TOTAL CALORIES FOR THE DAY: 621, INCLUDING 59 OF SNACKS

48	Breakfast	131	Lunch	383	Dinner
12	Diet cranberry juice	71	⅓ cup cottage cheese with	260	Cold filet of beef*
35	1 slice gluten toast	30	Tomato wedges	40	Cauliflower in foamy sauce*
1	1 teaspoon wild strawberry jam (diet)	30	1 fresh peach Iced tea	20	Carrots
			Midafternoon drink	63	Mocha Pot de Crème (page 52)
	Black coffee				Black coffee
1	Midmorning drink				
				58	6 oz. skim milk at bedtime

FILET MIGNON ROAST

Serves 8.   Calories per serving: 260. ■ *If you don't feel like having company so soon again, cut the filet in half and stow half in the freezer.*

LOW-CALORIE BARBECUE SAUCE. CALORIES PER CUP; 60.

½ cup tomato purée	2 tsp. Worcestershire sauce
½ cup water	2 tsp. prepared mustard
½ tsp. Sucaryl	2 tsps. celery salt
4 Tbs. lemon juice	

Mix all ingredients and simmer 15 minutes.

☞ Marinate the tenderloin in the barbecue sauce for 4 hours at room temperature. Place the tenderloin on a rack in a roasting pan and pour the marinade over it. Place in cold oven, heat to 400 degrees after the meat is in. Roast for 1 hour for medium rare, less for rare. Put meat on warm platter. Stir a little hot water into the pan, scrape up the juices, pour over meat.

[*continued*]

1 beef tenderloin (about 5 lbs.)	1 cup low-calorie barbecue sauce

CAULIFLOWER IN FOAMY SAUCE

Serves 6.   Calories per serving: 40.

1 medium-size cauliflower broken into flowerettes	1 Tbs. lemon juice
	Pinch nutmeg
2 eggs, separated	Pinch allspice
¼ cup skim milk	Salt and pepper to taste

☞ Cook the cauliflower in briskly boiling salted water for 10 minutes or until barely tender and drain. In the top of a double boiler over water that is only barely simmering, beat the egg yolks with all the remaining ingredients except the egg whites. Cook until thick, stirring constantly. Remove from heat and taste for seasoning. Beat the egg whites until stiff peaks form. Fold into the mixture and combine with the cauliflower.

TOTAL CALORIES FOR THE DAY: 603, INCLUDING 59 OF SNACKS

12	*Breakfast*	107	*Lunch*	425	*Dinner*
12	½ cup diet cranberry juice Black coffee	10	Beef bouillon on the rocks	375	Jellied Beef à la mode*
		50	6 cherrystone clams on the half shell	15	Coleslaw
				35	Fresh raspberries
1	Midmorning snack	38	Stuffed celery*		Black coffee
		9	Strawberry D-Zerta Iced tea	58	6 oz. skim milk at bedtime
			Midafternoon diet drink		

STUFFED CELERY STICKS NO. 2

Serves 4.   Calories per serving: 38.

8 inner stalks celery	2 drops Tabasco
⅓ cup low-fat cottage cheese	2 Tbs. diet Roquefort salad
Marjoram	dressing
Garlic powder	

☞ Put the celery sticks in ice water a few minutes to crisp. Drain and dry. Season the cottage cheese with marjoram and garlic powder to taste. Add 2 tablespoons diet Roquefort salad dressing. Blend well. Stuff the celery and sprinkle with paprika.

JELLIED BEEF À LA MODE

Serves 10.   Calories per serving: 375.   ■   *This is the night to entertain.*

4 lb. piece of beef, eye of round	¾ tsp. fresh thyme or ½ tsp. dried
⅓ cup cognac	1 small bay leaf
3 cups dry white wine	5 Tbs. chopped parsley
1 veal knuckle	6 carrots, quartered
¾ tsp. fresh chopped marjoram or ¼ tsp. dried	16 small onions (canned)
	2 tsp. gelatin
	3 Tbs. cold water

☞ Brown the beef on all sides in your Teflon pan. Warm the cognac, light it, and pour it flaming over the meat. When the flames have died down, add the wine, veal knuckle, salt, pepper, marjoram, thyme, bay leaf, and parsley and enough water to almost cover the beef. Cover, bring to a slow boil; turn down the heat and simmer for 1½ to 2 hours, or until the meat is almost tender. Add the carrots and continue cooking

[continued]

another 1/2 hour or until the meat is very tender. Skim out the carrots and arrange them with onions in the bottom of a mold. Slice the meat, not too thin, and arrange in layers over the vegetables. Sprinkle the gelatin over the cold water and let it stand 5 minutes. Add to it 2½ cups of the hot stock which has been carefully strained through a fine cloth. Pour over the meat and chill overnight. Unmold carefully on a chilled platter and garnish with parsley and tomato wedges. Don't throw away the rest of the stock. You can have it for lunch, or whenever—it is *so* good.

TOTAL CALORIES FOR THE DAY: 601, INCLUDING 59 OF SNACKS

130	*Breakfast*	135	*Lunch*	277	*Dinner*
95	2 slices crisp bacon	75	1 large artichoke vinaigrette	170	Ham mousse*
35	1 slice gluten toast	60	2 cinnamon cookies*	42	Harvard beets*
	Black coffee		Iced tea	25	Raw spinach and radish salad*
1	Midmorning drink		Midafternoon tea	40	Pineapple cheese dessert*
				58	6 oz. skim milk at bedtime

CINNAMON COOKIES
From Sucaryl pamphlet.

Makes 30 cookies. Calories: 30 each.

5 Tbs. butter	2 tsps. vanilla
1 cup flour, sifted	1 Tbs. milk, fruit juice, or
¼ tsp. baking powder	coffee
2 tsps. Sucaryl	1 tsp. cinnamon

☞ Cream butter until light and fluffy. Blend in the sifted flour and baking powder, mixed together. Mix or dissolve Sucaryl in combined vanilla and milk or other liquid. Stir in flour mixture and mix thoroughly. Sprinkle cinnamon over and knead in so there is a streaked appearance. Shape dough into balls about ½ inch in diameter, and place on Teflon cookie sheet. Flatten balls with a fork dipped in cold water. Bake in a 375-degree oven for 15 minutes, or until edges are nicely browned.

HAM MOUSSE

Serves 6.   Calories per serving: 170.

2 Tbs. gelatin	½ cup low-calorie mayonnaise
2 Tbs. Madeira	5 dashes Tabasco
2 tsps. lemon juice	1 cup diced ham
½ cup hot chicken broth	1 thin slice onion
2 eggs, separated	½ cup evaporated milk

☞ Get out the blender. Put the gelatin, wine, lemon juice, and hot chicken broth into the container and blend well. Add the yolks of the eggs, mayonnaise, Tabasco, ham, and onion to the blender mixture and blend for 20 seconds. Take off the top and slowly pour in the evaporated milk while the mixture is whirring. Beat the egg whites in a small bowl until they are

[continued]

stiff but not dry. Pour the mixtures from the blender into the egg whites and gently fold until everything is well combined. Pour into a medium-size mold and chill until set. Garnish with the usual rabbit food—carrot curls, radishes, pickle fans, what you will, just so it isn't full of calories.

HARVARD BEETS

Serves 4.   Calories per serving: 42.

1 #2 can beets	½ tsp. salt
1 Tbs. cornstarch	¼ cup cider vinegar
1 tsp. Sucaryl	

☞ Dice or slice beets, or buy them the way you want them. Combine cornstarch, Sucaryl, salt, and vinegar. Cook over low heat until thickened, stirring constantly. Add beets and heat until beets are hot.

RAW SPINACH AND RADISH SALAD

Calories per serving: 25.

☞ Take little tender new spinach leaves, break into bite-size pieces, and combine with lots and lots of thinly sliced radishes. Thin some diet Italian dressing with lemon juice and toss lightly.

PINEAPPLE CHEESE DESSERT

Serves 4.   Calories per serving: 40.

½ cup pineapple tidbits (diet pack)	4 Tbs. cottage cheese
	2 Tbs. orange juice

☞ Blend all ingredients. Put into 4 serving glasses, chill, and serve.

TOTAL CALORIES FOR THE DAY: 626, INCLUDING
59 OF SNACKS

79 *Breakfast*	188 *Lunch*	300 *Dinner*
27 ½ cup Puffed Rice	125 Chef's salad bowl* with chicken	150 Jellied salmon rings*
22 2 oz. skim milk		40 Whole tomato to slice at the table, à la Four Seasons*
30 1 sliced fresh peach	63 D-Zerta chocolate pudding	
Black coffee	Iced tea	
Midmorning drink	1 Low-calorie lemonade	15 Wrung-out cucumbers*
		90 3 stewed fresh plums
		Black coffee
		58 6 oz. skim milk at bedtime

CHEF'S SALAD BOWL

Serves 4.   Calories per serving: 125.

Salad greens	Fresh basil
4 thin slices dried beef	1 carrot, sliced
1 chicken breast Escabeche	1 stalk celery
8 raw mushrooms, sliced	1 tsp. sesame oil
4 artichoke hearts, sliced	1 medium onion, sliced
Whites of 2 hard-boiled eggs, julienne	Juice of 2 lemons
4 green pepper rings	2 dashes Tobasco
Minced onion	Thyme, fresh or dried

[continued]

☞ To a bowl of crisp salad greens, add the rest of the ingredients and dress with fresh lemon juice, 1 tablespoon sesame oil, and salt and pepper. To make the Chicken Escabeche, broil one breast of chicken on both sides to a golden brown and until three-quarters cooked. Put breast into casserole with sliced carrot, sliced celery, 1 teaspoon sesame oil, sliced onion, juice of 2 lemons, 2 dashes Tabasco. Sprinkle with fresh thyme. Cover and bake in a 375-degree oven for 10 minutes. Cool and slice for salad.

JELLIED SALMON RINGS

Serves 6.   Calories per serving: 150.

1 envelope unflavored gelatin	½ tsp. salt
¼ cup cold soup stock or water	¼ tsp. paprika
½ cup hot soup stock or water	1 Tbs. lemon juice
2 cups flaked salmon, cooked or canned	3 Tbs. low-fat cottage cheese
1 Tbs. minced parsley	1 bunch watercress
1 medium onion, chopped fine	

☞ Soften gelatin in cold liquid. Add hot liquid and stir until gelatin is dissolved. Chill until the consistency of unbeaten egg white. Mix salmon, parsley, onion, and seasoning. Blend lemon juice into cottage cheese and add to salmon mixture. Combine with gelatin mixture and pour into 6 individual ring molds and chill until firm. Unmold on beds of watercress.

WRUNG-OUT CUCUMBERS

☞ Half a cup equals 1 serving with 15 calories; will keep a long time in the refrigerator. (There must be a better name for these, but this seems to express the method as well as anything.) Peel and slice thinly as many cucumbers as you think you will want in the next few days. Place them in layers in a flat dish; sprinkle each layer well with salt. Weight them with a dish and place in the refrigerator for several hours. Turn them out onto a clean linen dishtowel. Roll them up and wring them until all the moisture is out. If they seem too salty, rinse them with cold water and wring them again. Pour on white vinegar to cover and chill again. We like them with freshly ground black pepper and dill weed.

For the Tomato à la Four Seasons: choose a large beefsteak tomato, place on a wooden board and serve 1 to each person, with a sharp knife. This is what they do at the Four Seasons, where it will cost you $2.50 for each tomato. See how thrifty I am?

Sweeten your fresh plums with Sucaryl—but I don't really have to tell you this, do I, after all these months?

TOTAL CALORIES FOR THE DAY: 610, INCLUDING 59 OF SNACKS

	Breakfast		Lunch		Dinner
105	*Breakfast*	187	*Lunch*	259	*Dinner*
70	Poached egg on	75	½ cup chicken	159	Smothered
35	1 slice gluten		salad		calf's liver*
	toast		Hawaiian*	53	Eggplant à la
	Black coffee	112	Floating island		Grecque*
1	Midmorning		with lemon	12	Cucumber
	drink		meringue		salad
			islands*	35	½ cup fresh
			Iced tea		raspberries
					Black coffee
			Midafternoon		
			goodie	58	6 oz. skim milk
					at bedtime

CHICKEN SALAD HAWAIIAN

Serves 2.   Calories per serving: 75.

1 poached chicken breast, cubed	½ cup celery, diced
½ cup diet pineapple chunks	2 Tbs. diet mayonnaise
	Lettuce leaves

☞ Mix all the ingredients together and pile into lettuce cups. Be sure to use pineapple chunks. Much better.

FLOATING ISLAND WITH
LEMON MERINGUE ISLANDS

Serves 6. Calories per serving: 112.

2 eggs	¼ tsp. salt
1 egg yolk	1 cup Old-Fashioned Apple-
2 cups milk	sauce
5 Tbs. sugar	1 tsp. vanilla extract

☞ Beat eggs and yolk until light. Blend in sugar and salt. Gradually stir in milk. Cook over hot water (not boiling) until mixture coats a metal spoon. Remove from heat, cool, and chill. Fold in the applesauce and vanilla. Serve in 6 sherbet glasses, topped with Lemon Meringue.

LEMON MERINGUE: Do this while the apple custard is chilling. Blend 1 egg white with ⅛ teaspoon salt and beat until mixture stands in soft peaks. Add 1 tablespoon sugar and ¼ teaspoon grated lemon rind. Beat until stiff. Drop mixture by tablespoons into hot water. Bake in a slow oven (325 degrees) 15 minutes.

SMOTHERED CALVES' LIVER

Serves 3. Calories per serving: 159.

¾ lb. calves' liver, sliced	½ clove garlic, pressed
½ cup tomato juice	¼ teaspoon salt
½ medium onion, grated	¼ teaspoon black pepper
½ small bay leaf, crushed	

☞ Marinate the liver in the tomato juice with the onion, garlic and seasonings for 15 minutes. Drain, reserving the liquid. Put liquid in skillet and bring to a quick boil. Add liver slices, reduce heat and cover. Simmer until tender, 5 to 8 minutes. Serve with the liquid as a sauce.

[*continued*]

EGGPLANT À LA GRÈCQUE

Serves 6.   Calories per serving: 53.

1 large eggplant (about 2 lbs.)	1 small bay leaf
2 tsps. lemon juice	¼ tsp. oregano
1 cup tomato juice	Salt and paprika to taste
2 canned pimentoes, chopped	1 hard-boiled egg, chopped
1 4-oz. can button mushrooms	

☞ Wash and dry eggplant. Do not peel. Dice in 1-inch cubes and sprinkle with lemon juice. Heat tomato juice and add all other ingredients except chopped egg. Mix well. Cover and simmer 20 minutes or until eggplant is tender. Remove bay leaf. Sprinkle with the egg before serving.

TOTAL CALORIES FOR THE DAY: 659, INCLUDING 59 OF SNACKS

	Breakfast		Lunch		Dinner
99	*Breakfast*	134	*Lunch*	367	*Dinner*
27	½ cup strawberries on	50	Cold cucumber soup*	282	Chicken breasts Grand Marnier*
50	½ cup cornflakes with	75	Small tomato stuffed with fresh crabmeat	12	Green beans
22	2 oz. skim milk Black coffee			15	Mixed green salad
		9	Lemon D-Zerta Iced tea	58	Apple mousse with faked whipped cream*
1	Midmorning snack		Midafternoon drink		Black coffee
				58	6 oz. skim milk at bedtime

COLD CUCUMBER SOUP

Serves 3. Calories per serving: 50.

1½ medium cucumbers or 1 large	1 small garlic clove, minced
¼ tsp. salt	2 cups buttermilk
	Minced parsley

☞ Peel and dice cucumbers. Rub glass bowl with a piece of garlic and the salt. Add the cucumbers and blend well. Add the minced garlic. Cover and chill for at least 1 hour. Sprinkle with minced parsley before serving. This looks beautiful in green crackly glass bowls.

CHICKEN BREASTS GRAND MARNIER

Serves 4. Calories per serving: 282.

2 whole chicken breasts (4)	1 Tbs. lemon juice
2 Tbs. butter	1 Tbs. frozen orange juice concentrate
1 tsp. salt	
½ tsp. paprika	1 egg yolk
1½ cups onion, chopped	3 Tbs. Grand Marnier
⅓ cup evaporated milk	

☞ Brown the chicken in the butter in the trusty Teflon pan. Sprinkle with salt and paprika. Spread half the onion in a lightly greased casserole; lay in the chicken, skin side up. Pour over the rest of the onion. Cover and bake 50 to 55 minutes in a 350-degree oven. Mix the evaporated milk, lemon juice, and frozen orange juice with the egg yolk and Grand Marnier. Drizzle over the chicken and bake uncovered 15 minutes more.

[continued]

APPLE MOUSSE WITH
FAKED WHIPPED CREAM

Serves 6.   Calories per serving: about 58.   ■   *Start with Old-Fashioned Applesauce:*

6 medium apples
Lemon juice to taste
Pinch of salt
Ground cinnamon
2 cups diet applesauce
2 Tbs. currant jelly
1 egg white, beaten stiff

1 recipe Faked Whipped
   Cream
Dash of cinnamon

FAKED WHIPPED CREAM
¼ cup cold water
1 Tbs. lemon juice
3 Tbs. nonfat dry milk
1 Tbs. Sucaryl

☞ Wash and core apples. Leave skins on. Simmer in covered pan in just enough water to keep them from scorching. When tender, put through a sieve or blender. Add lemon juice, salt, and cinnamon.

Pour the applesauce over the currant jelly and stir until the jelly is dissolved. Cool. Fold beaten egg white into cold applesauce. Pour into 6 sherbet glasses and chill at least 1 hour before serving. Top with 2½ tablespoons Faked Whipped Cream and a dash of cinnamon.

Chill all ingredients, including the bowl and beaters. Put everything in the 1-quart bowl of the electric mixer. Beat at high speed until thick enough to stand in peaks. Use at once. 5 calories per tablespoon.

TOTAL CALORIES FOR THE DAY: 624, INCLUDING
59 OF SNACKS

20	*Breakfast*	195	*Lunch*	350	*Dinner*
20	½ cup Mott's 5-Fruit Drink	20	Consommé Madrilene	288	California veal rolls*
	Black coffee	75	Cucumber boats*	20	Broccoli
1	Midmorning drink	100	Caramel custard (page 19)	15	Mixed green salad
			Iced tea	27	½ cup fresh strawberries
			Midafternoon tea	58	Black coffee
					6 oz. skim milk at bedtime

CUCUMBER BOATS

Serves 3. Calories per serving: 75.

3 large heavy cucumbers
Leftover cooked vegetables:
beets, string beans, carrots
1 tsp. capers

2 small gherkins, minced
1 hard-boiled egg, finely
chopped

☞ Pare the cucumbers and shape them into boats. If you want to be fancy, you can make baskets with handles, but that is harder. Mix the vegetables with some diet Italian dressing and fill the cucumbers. Arrange them on shredded lettuce and sprinkle with 1 finely chopped hard-boiled egg.

[*continued*]

CALIFORNIA VEAL ROLLS

Serves 3.   Calories per serving: 288.

1 lb. veal cutlet, cut into 3 slices	½ Tbs. green pepper, minced
	Salt and pepper
2 slices bacon	1 Tbs. lemon juice
½ cup soft breadcrumbs	½ tsp. poultry seasoning
1 Tbs. onion, grated	½ Tbs. flour
½ well-beaten egg	1 cup beef bouillon or stock
½ Tbs. parsley	½ cup black olives, thinly
½ Tbs. chives	sliced

☞ The slices of veal should be 3 inches long and 2 inches wide. Trim neatly and then grind the trimmings with the bacon and ½ cup soft breadcrumbs. To this mixture add the rest of the ingredients. Spread each strip of veal with ⅓ of the stuffing and roll into cylinders. Fasten securely with thread and/or toothpicks and brown on all sides in the Teflon pan. Lift out the rolls and add ½ tablespoon flour to the juice in the pan, stir until blended, and add 1 cup beef bouillon or stock. If it isn't brown enough, add a little Gravy Master. Stir until mixture just begins to thicken. Arrange the browned rolls in a shallow baking dish and pour the sauce over. Cover tightly and bake in a moderate oven for 35 minutes. Arrange the meat on a heated platter and stir the black olives into the sauce. Heat well and pour the sauce over the veal rolls which have had the strings and toothpicks removed. Dust with finely chopped parsley.

TOTAL CALORIES FOR THE DAY: 644, INCLUDING
59 OF SNACKS

190	*Breakfast*	170	*Lunch*	225	*Dinner*
190	Poached egg sort-of	100	Broiled calves' liver (page 8)	100	Shrimp in aspic*
	Benedict	20	Fresh asparagus	125	Diet delight sponge cake*
	Black coffee	50	Honeydew melon		Black coffee
1	Midmorning drink		Iced tea	58	6 oz. skim milk at bedtime
			Midafternoon tea		

POACHED EGG (sort-of Benedict)

½ English muffin, toasted   1 slice Canadian bacon,
1 poached egg   broiled

☞ Place toasted muffin on plate, cover with broiled Canadian bacon, top with poached egg. Serve hot.

SHRIMP IN ASPIC

Serves 6.   Calories per serving: 100.

1½ lbs. fresh shrimp
1 clove garlic, mashed
1 medium onion, sliced thin
6 peppercorns, gently bruised
1 bouquet garni (2 sprigs
    green celery leaves, 1
    sprig thyme, 2 cloves)
1 tsp. salt

1 small lemon, sliced thin
Tabasco
Black olives
Green pepper, finely
    chopped
1 tsp. gelatin
3 Tbs. cold water
2½ cups stock

[*continued*]

☞ Bring all the ingredients up to the black olives to a boil. Add the fresh shrimp and cook 10 to 12 minutes. Shell and devein; strain the stock into a fresh saucepan. Taste for seasoning and add 3 or 4 drops Tabasco. There should be only 2½ cups of stock.

ASPIC: Bring the stock slowly to a boil, remove from fire, and stir in 1 tablespoon plus 1 teaspoon gelatin which has been soaked for 5 minutes in 3 tablespoons cold water. When the gelatin is dissolved, strain it through a fine cloth into a fresh saucepan. Allow to cool to lukewarm. Arrange in a mold a layer of the cleaned, cooked shrimp. Pour a little of the gelatin mixture over them and allow to set. Then put a layer of thinly sliced black olives and more gelatin, let set, add more jelly, then a layer of shrimp, a layer of finely chopped green pepper, more shrimp, and more jelly. Chill 3 to 4 hours or overnight. When ready to serve, turn out onto a chilled platter and garnish with watercress and tomato slices and pickle fans.

DIET DELIGHT SPONGE CAKE

Serves 12.   Calories per serving: 125.

1⅓ cups sifted cake flour	½ tsp. vanilla
1½ tsps. baking powder	½ tsp. lemon extract
¼ tsp. salt	⅓ cup boiling water
3 eggs, separated	1 Tbs. 10X sugar
1 cup granulated sugar	

☞ Measure cake flour, baking powder, and salt into sifter. Beat egg whites until foamy white and double in volume in a large bowl. Sprinkle with ½ of the sugar, 1 tablespoon at a time, beating all the time, until the meringue forms soft peaks. Beat egg yolks with vanilla and lemon extract until fluffy thick in a medium size bowl: beat in the remaining ½ cup sugar, 1 tablespoon at a time, until mixture is creamy thick and forms soft peaks. Fold egg yolk mixture into egg white mixture until no streaks of white or yellow remain. Sift flour mixture, ¼ at a time, over top, gently fold in. Pour into an ungreased 9-inch tube pan. Bake in a 325-degree oven 55 minutes or until top springs back when gently pressed with a fingertip. Hang cake in pan on a bottle and cool completely. Loosen edges with a knife, turn out onto a plate, and sprinkle with the 10X sugar through a doily to make a pattern.

TOTAL CALORIES FOR THE DAY: 629, INCLUDING
59 OF SNACKS

155 *Breakfast*	200 *Lunch*	215 *Dinner*
35 ½ cup fresh papaya cubes	40 Deviled eggs in aspic ring*	150 4 oz. swordfish skewered à la Grècque*
50 3 slices lean Canadian bacon, broiled	50 Watercress and cherry tomatoes	20 Green beans
	130 Whitecap cheese cake*	15 Jellied lime-melon salad*
70 Egg cooked in Teflon pan so it looks like fried Black coffee	Iced tea	30 Small bunch seedless grapes Black coffee
	Midafternoon drink	
1 Midmorning drink		58 6 oz. skim milk at bedtime

DEVILED EGGS IN ASPIC RING

Serves 6. Calories per serving: 40. ■ *Have the ladies over for lunch beside the pool.*

THE ASPIC (make this first)

1 envelope plain gelatin	¼ cup dry white wine
¼ cup cold water	1 Tbs. tarragon vinegar
1 tsp. chicken stock base	¼ tsp. salt
1⅓ cups fat-free chicken broth	6 pitted green olives cut in two

☞ Soak the gelatin in the cold water. Add the chicken stock base to the chicken broth and bring to a boil. Remove from the heat and add the soaked gelatin. Stir until dissolved; add wine and vinegar. Chill until it begins to set. Pour about ½ inch of the aspic into the bottom of small ring mold. Lay the stuffed egg halves (see below) at evenly spaced intervals, stuffed side down. Put 2 half olives between each 2 eggs, cut side up. Spoon the remaining gelatin over and around the eggs and chill until firm. Unmold on a serving plate and garnish with sprigs of watercress. Fill middle with cherry tomatoes.

THE EGGS

3 hard-boiled eggs, halved
1 Tbs. low-calorie mayonnaise
½ tsp. Worcestershire sauce
½ tsp. Dijon mustard
½ tsp. onion salt
Dash cayenne pepper

☞ Mash egg yolks with mayonnaise and seasonings. Stuff egg whites with mixture.

WHITECAP CHEESE CAKE

Serves 10.   Calories per serving: 130.

2 eggs
1 cup water
¼ tsp. salt
2 Tbs. Sucaryl
2 envelopes unflavored gelatin
⅓ cup instant dried skim milk
1 tsp. grated lemon rind

3 Tbs. lemon juice
1 tsp. vanilla
3 cups (1½ lbs.) cream style cottage cheese
1 cup evaporated milk, well chilled
3 Tbs. graham cracker crumbs

☞ Separate eggs, putting whites in small bowl and yolks in a second small bowl. Beat egg yolks slightly, beat in water and salt. Add Sucaryl. Mix gelatin and dried milk in the top of a double boiler. Stir in egg yolk mixture. Cook over simmering water, stirring constantly, for about 5 minutes, or until gelatin completely dissolves. When mixture coats a metal spoon, strain into a large bowl. Add lemon rind, 2 tablespoons lemon juice.

[*continued*]

Press cottage cheese through a sieve. Stir into gelatin mixture until blended. Beat egg whites until they stand in firm peaks. Beat chilled evaporated milk with remaining 1 tablespoon lemon juice until stiff. Fold egg whites, then milk into cheese mixture. Pour into 8-cup mold. Chill at least 4 hours. Unmold onto serving plate. Press cracker crumbs around edge. Garnish with fresh strawberries or raspberries.

SWORDFISH SKEWERED
À LA GRÈCQUE

Serves 3. Calories per serving: 150.

1 lb. swordfish cut in 1-inch-thick slice, cut in 1-inch pieces	½ tsp. salt
	Pepper
¼ cup lemon juice	1 Tbs. chopped parsley
1 Tbs. salad oil	Bay leaves

☞ Mix everything except the bay leaves together and allow to marinate at least 1 hour. Drain the swordfish and string the cubes on skewers with a small bay leaf between each 2 cubes of fish. Boil for 8 to 10 minutes and serve sprinkled with parsley and garnished with lemon wedges.

JELLIED LIME-MELON SALAD

☞ Use D-Zerta lime gelatin and put honeydew melon balls in each mold. Garnish with watercress.

TOTAL CALORIES FOR THE DAY: 639, INCLUDING
59 OF SNACKS

25	Breakfast	225	Lunch	330	Patio Dinner
25	½ cup tomato juice	150	4 oz. broiled chicken breast	70	Gazpacho (page 188)
	Black coffee	30	Pickled beet salad	170	London broil*
1	Midmorning drink	20	½ cup string beans	15	Mixed green salad
		25	Coffee gelatin dessert	75	Fresh fruit plate
			Iced tea		1 apricot
			Midafternoon drink		4 strawberries
					6 cherries
					2 pineapple spears
					Iced coffee
				58	6 oz. skim milk at bedtime

LONDON BROIL

☞ This London broil can be served hot, cold, or room temperature, depending on your mood and the weather. We had this on a hot day on a shady terrace overlooking a swimming pool. The London broil has been marinated in diet salad dressing for several hours with garlic-flavored monosodium glutamate. It was broiled about an hour before serving time. No one who was there suspected that this was a diet lunch except the dear lady who was dieting and the hostess (me!).

TOTAL CALORIES FOR THE DAY: 577, INCLUDING
59 OF SNACKS

20 *Breakfast*	107 *Lunch*	391 *Dinner*
20 1 cup rhubarb Black coffee	26 Bouillon imperial*	286 Baked stuffed lobster*
1 Midmorning drink	72 Antipasto plate*	50 Stewed tomatoes
	9 Cherry D-Zerta Iced tea	20 Raw mushroom salad*
	Midafternoon tea	55 Melon balls and straw- berries Black coffee
		58 6 oz. skim milk at bedtime

BOUILLON IMPERIAL

Serves 3.   Calories per serving: 26.

> 1 can condensed beef broth
> ½ cup water

> ¼ cup thinly sliced carrots
> ¼ cup thinly sliced celery

☞ Combine all ingredients in a medium-size saucepan. Heat to boiling. Cover and simmer 10 minutes, or until vegetables are just crisply tender.

ANTIPASTO PLATE

Serves 3.   Calories per serving: 72.

½ pkg. frozen asparagus spears
½ Tbs. cider vinegar
½ tsp. olive oil
½ Tbs. capers and liquid
   Lettuce
3 oz. can pimentos, drained
1 small can mushroom caps,
   drained

3 small slices bologna
3 green onions
3 radishes
3 stalks celery cut into 4-inch
   lengths

☞ Cook asparagus in boiling salted water. Drain. Place in flat dish, sprinkle with vinegar, oil, capers. Chill. At serving time, line 3 salad plates with lettuce, arrange the asparagus, pimentos, mushrooms, and bologna, divided evenly, on the plates. Garnish with the remaining vegetables. Extra vinegar can be drizzled over if desired.

BAKED STUFFED LOBSTER

Serves 4. Calories per serving: 286.

4 small live lobsters, 1¼ lbs.
   each
2 tsp. grated onion
1 Tbs. butter
¼ cup flour
1 envelope instant chicken
   broth
½ lb. fresh mushrooms,
   chopped

2 cups skim milk
4 tsps. lemon juice
⅓ cup unsalted cracker
   crumbs
¼ cup Parmesan cheese
   Paprika

☞ Drop live lobsters in a very large kettle of rapidly boiling water. Cover. Cook over high heat 8 to 10 minutes. Remove at once with tongs. Drain until cool enough to handle. Remove meat from each lobster, saving shell for restuffing. Crack claws and remove meat. Save the coral, if any. Cut lobster meat in small dices. Set shells on cookie sheet. Sauté lob-

[continued]

ster meat and onions in Teflon pan with the butter for 2 minutes. Stir in flour, chicken broth, mushrooms and liquid, and milk. Cook, stirring constantly, until mixture thickens and boils, 1 minute. Remove from heat. Stir in lemon juice. Spoon into lobster shells. Mix cracker crumbs and cheese. Sprinkle over lobster mixture; dust with paprika. Bake in a very hot oven (450 degrees) 10 minutes, or until bubbly.

RAW MUSHROOM SALAD

Serves 4.   Calories per serving: 20.

1 dozen mushrooms, sliced very thin	½ cup onion, minced
1 cup celery stalks, minced fine	½ tsp. freshly cracked pepper
	1 tsp. salad oil
	Juice of 3 lemons

☞ Toss and add ¼ cup diced pimento and ½ medium chopped truffle. Serve in lettuce cups.

TOTAL CALORIES FOR THE DAY: 613, INCLUDING
58 OF SNACKS

85	*Breakfast*	191	*Lunch*	279	*Dinner*
33	¾ cup diet puffed rice cereal	55	Summer garden salad	190	Baked chicken*
				12	Green beans
		136	Fresh raspberries	15	Watercress and radishes
22	2 oz. skim milk				
30	1 fresh peach		Frannie*	62	Jellied ambrosia*
	Black coffee		Tea with lemon		Black coffee
	Midmorning drink		Midafternoon tea		
				58	6 oz. skim milk at bedtime

FRESH RASPBERRIES FRANNIE

Serves 1. Calories per serving: 136. ■ *This comes under the heading of pure summer. Frannie introduced us to this on her porch one hot night in July and once a year, diet or no diet, we will splurge.*

1 cup raspberries
2 Tbs. half-and-half sour cream

1 Tbs. brown sugar

☞ Just eat and enjoy.

[*continued*]

BAKED CHICKEN

Serves 5.   Calories per serving: 190.

3 lb. chicken, cut for frying
Juice of 2 limes
Juice of 1 lemon
⅓ cup white wine
1 clove garlic, minced

1 tsp. salt
¼ tsp. dried thyme
⅛ tsp. pepper
1 Tbs. butter

☞ Combine the lime and lemon juices, wine, garlic, salt, thyme, and pepper. Lay the chicken pieces in a shallow casserole and pour the mixture over them. Let stand at room temperature 30 minutes, or 1 to 2 hours in the refrigerator. Remove the chicken pieces from the marinade and arrange them in a shallow baking pan so that they will not overlap— that is, so that they are in a single layer. Dot them with the butter and bake in a 425-degree oven 1 hour or until tender. Baste every 10 minutes with the leftover marinade. Pour the pan juices over the chicken before serving.

JELLIED AMBROSIA

Serves 4.   Calories per serving: 60.

1 envelope plain gelatin
¼ cup cold water
¼ cup boiling water
1½ tsps. Sucaryl
1½ cups diet orange drink

1 Tbs. lemon juice
2 oranges, skinned and
  sectioned
1 banana, sliced
3 Tbs. flaked coconut

☞ Sprinkle the gelatin on the cold water and dissolve in boiling water. Stir in the Sucaryl, orange drink, and lemon juice. Chill until syrupy. Fold the oranges, banana, and coconut into the gelatin mixture and chill until firm.

TOTAL CALORIES FOR THE DAY: 602, INCLUDING
59 OF SNACKS

12 *Breakfast*	139 *Lunch*	392 *Dinner*

12 Cranberry juice
   Black coffee
	100 Striped bass
	     with fennel
	     (4 oz.)*
		250 Beef tenderloin
		     en ficelle*

1 Midmorning
   ice-cold root
   beer
	30 Cucumbers and
	     tomato cubes
	     in yogurt
		35 Green beans
		     almondine
		     (page 32)

	9 Orange D-Zerta
	   Iced tea
		50 Orange, grape-
		     fruit, and
		     endive salad

	Midafternoon
	tea
		57 Biscuit
		   Tortoni
		   (page 189)
		   Black coffee

		58 6 oz. skim milk at bedtime

STRIPED BASS WITH FENNEL

Serves 6. Calories per 4-oz. serving: 100.

1 large cleaned striped bass	6 oz. white wine
(about 6 lbs.)	Juice of 4 lemons
Dried fennel	1 onion, finely minced
Fresh fennel	2 Tbs. brandy

☞ Take a large cleaned striped bass, weighing about 6 lbs.
Put some dried fennel stalks in the stomach after you have
salted the inside of the fish. Bake in a 350-degree oven for
about 20 minutes to a golden brown, in 6 oz. white wine,

[continued]

lemon juice, and onions and 1 tablespoon chopped green fennel. Spread a layer of the dried fennel on a large platter and place the fish on top. Sprinkle the bass and fennel with warmed brandy, then flame. Filet the fish. Pass the liquid as sauce.

BEEF TENDERLOIN

Serves 3.   Calories per serving: 250.

1 qt. very strong beef consommé	14 oz. very lean tenderloin of beef
1 carrot, diced	1 Tbs. Dijon mustard
1 onion, diced	3 Tbs. of the beef consommé
3 celery stalks	1 tsp. beurre manie (1 tsp.
Cracked pepper	each butter and flour
Bay leaf	mixed)

☞ Bring the consommé and vegetables to a boil and simmer for 15 minutes. Wrap string around a 14-oz. very lean beef tenderloin. Have the string long enough so that you have an end hanging out of the pot. Lower the filet into the broth and simmer for about 5 or 6 minutes for rare, longer for medium to well done. Remove from broth and slice rather thinly for serving. Serve with the sauce on the side.

TOTAL CALORIES FOR THE DAY: 686, INCLUDING
58 OF SNACKS

92	*Breakfast*	226	*Lunch*	310	*Dinner*
20	¼ cup blue-berries	36	Celery root remoulade*	205	Salmon steak
50	½ cup Wheaties	160	Egg Floren-tine* (page 58)	40	Cold tomato stuffed with minced celery and cucumber
22	2 oz. skim milk Black coffee				
	Midmorning drink	30	Small bunch white grapes Iced tea	10	Watercress
				55	Melon balls and straw-berries*
			Midafternoon refreshment		Black coffee
				58	6 oz. skim milk at bedtime

CELERY ROOT REMOULADE

Serves 6.   Calories per serving: 36.

1 large celery root (celeriac)	½ tsp. salt
2 Tbs. lemon juice	Dash cayenne pepper
¼ cup Dijon mustard	1½ Tbs. olive oil

☞ Peel celery root and blanch in salted boiling water for 5 minutes. Drain and chill in the refrigerator. When chilled, cross-slice into long, slender pieces. Beat together the lemon juice, mustard, salt, pepper, cayenne pepper, and olive oil. Immediately before serving, give the dressing an extra beating
[continued]

and pour over the celery-root slivers. Keep turning the celery root so that it soaks up as much dressing as possible.

MELON BALLS AND STRAWBERRIES

Serves 1. Calories: 55.

> ½ cup melon balls   ½ cup strawberries
> 1 Tbs. fresh orange juice   Mint leaves

☞ Blend ingredients and sweeten with a little Sucaryl if you like things sweet. Chill for at least an hour. Garnish with mint sprigs.

TOTAL CALORIES FOR THE DAY: 652, INCLUDING 58 OF SNACKS

	Breakfast		*Lunch*		*Dinner*
49		120		425	
12	½ cup cranberry juice	15	Jellied consommé	285	Arabian knights*
35	1 slice gluten toast	66	3 oz. seviche of bay scallops*	75	Eggplant casserole*
2	Wild strawberry jam (dietetic)	30	Sliced beef-steak tomato	15	Mixed green salad
	Black coffee	9	Lime D-Zerta Iced tea	50	Melon Black coffee
	Midmorning drink		Midafternoon drink	58	6 oz. skim milk at bedtime

SEVICHE OF BAY SCALLOPS

Serves 3.   Calories per serving: 66.   ■ *Do the day before.*

½ lb. tiny bay scallops
Enough fresh lime juice to
    cover
1 Tbs. chili sauce
2 Tbs. orange juice
3 dashes Tabasco

1 Tbs. green pepper, thinly
    sliced
2 Tbs. Spanish onion,
    julienne
¼ tsp. salt
Lettuce leaves

☞ Marinate the scallops in lime juice. Cover and place in refrigerator overnight. In a separate bowl, mix ½ cup of the scallop marinade, 1 tablespoon chili sauce, 2 tablespoons orange juice, 3 dashes Tabasco, 1 tablespoon thinly sliced green pepper, 2 tablespoons julienne Spanish onion, ¼ teaspoon salt. Arrange scallops in a cocktail glass on a lettuce leaf and pour sauce over them.

ARABIAN KNIGHTS

Serves 4.   Calories per serving: 285.

1 clove of garlic, minced
1 lb. very lean lamb, ground
1 small onion, minced
1½ tsps. yogurt

1 tsp. curry powder
¼ tsp. salt
1 tsp. lemon juice

☞ Mix all the ingredients very thoroughly. Divide into 8 portions and pat each around a skewer in a long cigar shape. Cook over hot coals until brown all over.

[*continued*]

EGGPLANT CASSEROLE

Serves 3 or 4.   Calories per serving: 75.

1 small eggplant	1 tsp. salt
Boiling salted water	½ tsp. freshly ground black
1 Tbs. olive oil	pepper
2 large onions, peeled and	½ bay leaf
sliced	⅛ tsp. basil
1 clove garlic, pressed	⅛ tsp. oregano
½ lb. fresh mushrooms	Pinch powdered cloves
2 large tomatoes, peeled and	Sprinkle of Parmesan
chopped	
1 green pepper, seeded and	
cut in strips	

☞ Preheat oven to 275 degrees. Peel the eggplant and cut into 1-inch slices. Cover with boiling water and simmer ten minutes. Drain well. Heat the oil, and the onions and garlic, and sauté in the Teflon pan until lightly browned. Remove stems from the mushrooms and save for another use. Add mushroom caps to the onions and garlic and cook, stirring, an additional 5 minutes. Add the tomatoes, green pepper, salt, pepper, herbs and spices, and simmer 10 minutes. Place alternating layers of eggplant and other vegetables in a 1-quart casserole, sprinkle with Parmesan, and bake for 1¼ hours.

TOTAL CALORIES FOR THE DAY: 662, INCLUDING
58 OF SNACKS

120	*Breakfast*	205	*Lunch*	279	*Dinner*
50	½ cup orange juice	175	⅓ cup cottage cheese mixed with onions, radishes, and green pepper on 1 slice dark pumpernickel	150	Asparagus-chicken salad*
70	1 soft boiled egg			100	Artichoke vinaigrette (page 18)
	Black coffee			29	Strawberry sponge*
	Midmorning drink	30	Small bunch seedless grapes		Black coffee
			Iced tea or coffee	58	6 oz. skim milk at bedtime
			Midafternoon drink		

ASPARAGUS-CHICKEN SALAD

Serves 4.   Calories per serving: 150.

1 lb. fresh asparagus	⅛ tsp. pepper
Boiling salted water	½ cup diet mayonnaise
2½ cups cooked chicken, diced	1 Tbs. lemon juice
⅓ cup celery, diced	Watercress
⅛ tsp. celery seed	Tomato wedges
½ tsp. salt	

☞ Clean asparagus thoroughly and break off bottom ends.
Cover and cook in 1 inch boiling water over low heat 12 to 15

[*continued*]

minutes. Drain and chill. Combine chicken, celery, celery seed, salt and pepper. Dice asparagus, reserving tips for garnish. Add remaining asparagus to chicken mixture. Blend mayonnaise and lemon juice together and add to the chicken mixture. Toss lightly but thoroughly. Spoon into crisp watercress and garnish with tomato wedges and the asparagus tips.

STRAWBERRY SPONGE

Serves 6.   Calories per serving: 29.

1 envelope unflavored gelatin
½ cup cold water
1 Tbs. Sucaryl

1½ Tbs. lemon juice
1 pint strawberries, crushed
2 egg whites

Soften gelatin in water in the top of a double boiler. Add Sucaryl and lemon juice. Heat, stirring, until gelatin dissolves. Remove from heat and add crushed berries. Let stand until mixture begins to thicken. Beat until light and fluffy. Beat egg whites until stiff. Fold into the gelatin mixture. Spoon into 6 individual molds or a 3-cup mold. Chill until firm.

AUTUMN MENUS

For me, autumn is a time of beginning. School begins in September, the family regroups after a summer of varied travels, the telephone rings constantly as the committees abandoned in June reconvene to start another season's work. The heavy clothes are retrieved from storage, tried on, and hopefully taken to the dressmaker to be taken in. If it has to be the other way—let out—you should be starting your diet regime. It is more difficult to diet in this quarter of the year, I think. You are assailed with social duties, luncheons, dinners, teas, and meetings, each simply festooned with calories. Your strength must be as the strength of ten: your will power must be reinforced with all available aids. This book is one way, but there are other things to help you, too. Food, for instance. The new apple crop is ready and there is no other time in the year that apples are as crisp and juicy as when they first come into the market. An apple and a half-ounce of Camembert cheese is a great dessert; or a baked apple, made hearty with cinnamon, hits the spot on the first cold evening. An orange-red persimmon can be cut in half, sprinkled with fresh lime juice, and eaten with a spoon, at 75 calories for a brilliant ending to your meal. Fresh cranberries sparkle in the market, but if you are lazy the Ocean Spray people have a delicious low-calorie cranberry sauce in cans.

Bay scallops are in their peak supply in late fall, cheaper then; and red cabbage is another colorful addition to your autumn table. Salad greens are more mature and have a heavier flavor, so make your salad dressings spicier and sharper to counteract. Cherry tomatoes seem to be a year-round thing right now. As an accompaniment to the cocktail hour they are superb. I *know* you are not drinking, but others, more fortunate and skinnier than you, may very well be, as you imbibe your low-calorie drink.

If the budget is dragging again this is the time to have an old hen for dinner. Fricassee of chicken is a standby in our house. The skinnies get dumplings with theirs, while dieters bravely eat their three ounces of white meat.

When Thanksgiving arrives, join the group joyously and dine on turkey, squash, boiled onions (*without* cream sauce; sorry), diet cranberry sauce, and pumpkin soufflé. Or eat some Emperor grapes with two walnuts for dessert.

Christmas is another crisis—at least in the diet department —but you will meet the challenge with all the wit and ingenuity you are capable of finding deep in your little fat soul. Turkey is really the best festive main course for you to choose; or a big standing rib roast of beef. Your serving will look infinitesimal because we all overeat during the winter holidays, so surround it with braised celery, oven-browned onions, and Brussels sprouts. If you have real courage and also love for your relatives and guests, make Yorkshire pudding and serve everyone but yourself. This is what is known as self-sacrifice, and it will pay off when you find the pounds and inches melting away. Give this gift to yourself—good health and a more slender figure.

Autumn Menus

Main dishes for dinner

⋖§ WEEK 1 §⋗

Baked chicken
Oriental pork with Chinese vegetables
Baked ham
Egg Gennaro
Stuffed beef bundles
Crisp baked chicken
Shrimp with bacon blankets

⋖§ WEEK 2 §⋗

Calves' liver
Fish filets with egg sauce
Chicken Kikkoman
Lamb on rotisserie
Shrimp gumbo
Meatballs with mushroom sauce
Steak teriyaki

⋖§ WEEK 3 §⋗

Lamb Fasaalia
Pepper steak

253

Corned beef and cabbage
Veal chop en casserole
Poulet en pot
Sweet and sour tongue
Armenian beefburgers

❧ WEEK 4 ❧

Shish kebab
Brown lamb stew
Fish filets almondine
Hamburger ring
Pork tenderloin stuffed with prunes
Broiled lobster
Veal Parmesan

❧ WEEK 5 ❧

Spanish chicken
Grilled kidney and bacon
Oysters en brochette
Stuffed beefburger
Sweetbreads and mushrooms
Lamb spareribs with sauerkraut
Lamb chop creole

❧ WEEK 6 ❧

Cod à la Portuguaise
Beef stew Gaston
Bouillabaisse
Dolmas
Ham, egg, and vegetable bake
Leg of lamb, eastern Mediterranean style
Flamenco veal chops

TOTAL CALORIES FOR THE DAY: 606

75	*Breakfast*	229	*Lunch*	302	*Dinner*
75	1 scrambled egg	70	Gazpacho (page	221	Broiled chicken
	Black coffee		188)	23	Carrots juli-
		150	Tuna fish salad		enne
	Midmorning	9	Orange D-Zerta	15	Salad
	drink		Tea with lemon	43	½ cup blue-
					berries
			Midafternoon		Black coffee
			refreshment		
					Nothing but
					some low-
					calorie
					ginger ale
					tonight,
					honey.

☞ Make the tuna fish salad with diet mayonnaise, celery, onions, and 2 ounces of diet-pack tuna.

The chicken is plain broiled chicken. It can be brushed with a little diet salad dressing. Half a small broiler or a quarter of a larger one. You are on your honor!

TOTAL CALORIES FOR THE DAY: 610, INCLUDING 59 OF SNACKS

70	*Breakfast*	180	*Lunch*	301	*Dinner*
70	1 soft-boiled egg Black coffee	45	4 oz. Vichysoisse (page 203)	274	Oriental pork with Chinese vegetables*
1	Midmorning low-calorie drink	100	2 oz. corned beef	27	Orange pineapple sherbet*
		5	Dill pickle with watercress and radishes		Tea or coffee, if you must
		30	1 fresh peach Tea with lemon	58	6 oz. skim milk at bedtime
			Midafternoon tea		

☞ Make a pretty delicatessen plate with your corned beef and vegetables for lunch.

ORIENTAL PORK WITH CHINESE VEGETABLES

Serves 3.   Calories per serving: 274.

¾ lb. lean boneless pork (we
used loin)
2 Tbs. soy sauce
3 oz. unsweetened pineapple
juice
½ cup water
¼ lb. green beans cut in 1-inch
pieces
1 large yellow squash, quar-

tered and cut in 2-inch
long pieces
1 Tbs. cornstarch
1 Tbs. cold water
1 can water chestnuts, sliced
thin
1 pkg. frozen snow pea pods
6 cherry tomatoes
Steamed celery cabbage

☞ Trim all the fat from the pork, then cut in thin strips. Place in a shallow dish. Drizzle with soy sauce, let stand about 15 minutes, then drain. Sauté the strips in a Teflon frying pan about 5 minutes. Stir in the pineapple juice and water. Cover and simmer for 1 hour. Place green beans and squash sticks around meat. Cook 15 minutes longer. Smooth cornstarch and water to a paste in a cup. Stir into the meat mixture and cook, stirring constantly, for about 5 minutes. Then place on top the thinly sliced water chestnuts and the pea pods, which have been defrosted. Cover and warm the vegetables. Spoon onto heated plates. Spoon the steamed cabbage around the edges and garnish with cherry tomatoes.

ORANGE PINEAPPLE SHERBET

20 servings, ½ cup each. Calories per serving: 58 ■ *This makes a lot, but just tuck it in your freezer. You can have some before bed instead of milk.*

1 6-oz. can frozen orange juice concentrate	3½ cups cold water
1 6-oz. can frozen pineapple juice concentrate	2 Tbs. Sucaryl
	1 cup non-fat dry milk

☞ Set refrigerator control at coldest. Put all ingredients into a 2-quart mixing bowl in order given. Beat just enough to blend. Pour into ice-cub trays and freeze 1 to 2 hours until half frozen. Remove to a large chilled mixing bowl; beat on low speed until the mixture is softened. Then beat on high speed 3 to 5 minutes until creamy but not liquid. Pour into freezer containers and freeze.

TOTAL CALORIES FOR THE DAY: 633, INCLUDING
59 OF SNACKS

105 Breakfast	100 Lunch	369 Dinner
70 Poached egg on	75 2 oz. cottage	212 Baked ham
35 1 slice gluten	cheese with	80 Pseudo sweet
toast	2 tomato	potato puff
Black coffee	slices,	(page 144)
	cucumbers	12 Green beans
1 Midmorning	and lettuce	15 Salad
drink	25 Grape gelatin*	50 ½ cup fresh
	Tea with lemon	pineapple
		Black coffee
	Midafternoon	
	break	58 6 oz. skim
		milk
		at bedtime

GRAPE GELATIN

Serves 6.   Calories per serving: 25.

1 Tbs. gelatin   ¾ cup grape juice
¼ cup cold water   1 Tbs. lemon juice
¾ cup boiling water   ¼ tsp. Sucaryl

 Soften the gelatin in ¼ cup cold water, then add the hot water. Stir until dissolved. Add the rest of the ingredients, stir, and chill in molds. Or use Mr. Wiggle. It comes in assorted, exotic flavors.

A slice of ham, ¼ inch thick, 3 by four inches, equals 212 calories,—and see that you remove ALL the fat.

TOTAL CALORIES FOR THE DAY: 674, INCLUDING
59 OF SNACKS

63	*Breakfast*	237	*Lunch*	315	*Dinner*
28	½ cup Mott's Grape Apple Drink	175	1 small broiled hamburger patty	25	1 cup jellied consommé
35	1 slice gluten toast	35	Sliced tomato and red onion slices with vinegar and freshly ground black pepper	160	Tomato stuffed with lobster*
1	Midmorning low-calorie drink			10	Watercress
				20	Artichoke hearts
		27	½ cup fresh strawberries Tea with lemon	100	Blueberry mousse* Black coffee
			Midafternoon tea	58	6 oz. skim milk at bedtime

TOMATO STUFFED WITH LOBSTER

Serves 1.   Calories per serving: 160.

☞ For each serving you must have a large, thoroughly ripe tomato. It should have the seeds removed, as well as the pulp, and be very well drained. Into the tomato put a bit of chopped basil, a bit of salt, and then a large medallion of lobster, (about ⅓ of a cup) which has been perfectly cooked and cooled. It is possible to use canned lobster, but it is not half as good. Did you ever hear of anyone having lobster left over? To get back to the recipe. Top the lobster with 1 cold poached egg, well

[continued]

trimmed. Garnish this with finely chopped lobster and parsley and serve with the following dressing: Combine 1½ cups low-calorie mayonnaise with a touch of garlic, 1 anchovy filet chopped fine, and a dash of lemon juice. Use 1 tablespoon per serving after the ingredients have mellowed several hours. This is a perfect dish for warm days and one that you can prepare in the morning and serve later.

BLUEBERRY MOUSSE

Serves 6.   Calories per serving: 100.

1 cup blueberries	1 Tbs. Sucaryl
1 Tbs. gelatin	Pinch salt
¼ cup cold water	2 eggs, separated
1 cup skim milk	1 cup farmer cheese broken
1 Tbs. cornstarch	in pieces

☞ Dissolve the gelatin in cold water. Add the gelatin to the milk. Heat the milk in the top of a double boiler. Make a paste of the cornstarch with a little cold water and add the hot milk, stirring until slightly thickened. Beat the Sucaryl, salt, and egg yolks together. Add to the hot mixture a little at a time, stirring constantly so it won't curdle, then put aside to cool. Put the farmer cheese into the blender, adding enough, but not all, of the milk mixture to insure easy blending. Then mix everything together. Beat the egg whites until stiff peaks form. Fold them into the first mixture with the blueberries. Pour into a ring mold and chill a few hours before unmolding.

TOTAL CALORIES FOR THE DAY: 604, INCLUDING
59 OF SNACKS

105	*Breakfast*	135	*Lunch*	305	*Dinner*
105	Poached egg on gluten toast	30	Consommé Bellevue*	218	Stuffed beef bundles*
	Black coffee	60	Artichoke towers*	50	Celery root remoulade (page 245)
1	Midmorning drink	20	Radishes, about 4 Greek olives	37	Jellied orange juice*
		25	Lemonade sherbet* Tea with lemon		Black coffee
			Midafternoon tea	58	6 oz. skim milk at bedtime

CONSOMMÉ BELLEVUE

Serves 3.   Calories per serving: 30.

1 can S. S. Pierce chicken broth	Salt
1 bottle (6 oz.) Doxie clam juice	Pepper
Nutmeg	Juice of 1 lemon

☞ Chill the chicken broth to facilitate removing every bit
of fat. Combine the broth with the other ingredients and bring
to the boiling point.

[*continued*]

ARTICHOKE TOWERS

Serves 3.   Calories per serving: 60.

1 can tomato aspic	2 hard-boiled eggs
1 can artichoke bottoms	1 Tbs. diet mayonnaise

☞ Place 3 thin slices aspic on a salad plate garnished with watercress. Place an artichoke bottom on each slice and top with a thin slice of hard-boiled egg. Put a teaspoon of diet mayonnaise on top.

LEMONADE SHERBET

Serves 6.   Calories per serving: 25.

1 5-oz. can Libby's low-calorie frozen lemonade	Grated rind of 1 lemon
3 cans water	2 or 3 egg whites

☞ Mix the lemonade with the water and 1 grated lemon rind and freeze until slushy. Add the egg whites and beat well. Return to freezer until slushy again, beat again, then freeze. Or throw it in the blender and serve right away. Looks like a frozen daiquiri in a champagne glass. Put a fresh strawberry on top.

STUFFED BEEF BUNDLES

Serves 3.   Calories per serving: 218.

1 piece lean boneless round steak weighing about ¾ lb.	1 small onion, chopped (¼ cup)
1 small can chopped mushrooms	1 Tbs. ketchup
	Salt and pepper
	1 medium carrot, pared and

cut in thin 4-inch-long   1 envelope instant beef broth
strips   ½ cup water

☞ Pound the steak very thin with a mallet and cut in 3
equal sized pieces. Trim all fat. Drain mushrooms, saving
liquid in can. Mix mushrooms with onion, catsup, salt, and
pepper in a small bowl. Spread evenly on steak slices. Place
carrot sticks, dividing evenly, crosswise at the end of each roll.
Roll up like a jelly roll and fasten with a couple of toothpicks.
Brown rolls in a Teflon pan, add the mushroom liquid, beef
broth, and simmer, covered, for 1¼ hours. Remove to a heated
serving platter. Pour juices from the pan into a 1-cup measure.
Skim off any fat. Measure 1 tablespoon of fat and return to
pan. Add water to make 1 cup. Stir in 1 tablespoon Wondra
flour into fat in pan. Add meat juice mixture. Cook, stirring,
until gravy thickens and boils, 1 minute. If it isn't brown
enough, add a little Gravy Master. How *long* is it since you've
had gravy?

CELERY ROOT REMOULADE, (page 245), keeps very well, as you
may have found out, so perhaps there is still a serving lurking
in the back of the refrigerator.

JELLIED ORANGE JUICE

Serves 4.   Calories per serving: 37.

       1 Tbs. unflavored gelatin   1 cup orange juice
       ½ tsp. Sucaryl   1 Tbs. lemon juice
       ¼ tsp. salt

☞ Soften gelatin in ¼ cup cold water. Add ½ cup boiling
water and stir until dissolved. Add Sucaryl and salt. Stir. Add
orange juice and lemon juice. Chill in refrigerator until the
consistency of raw egg white. Stir and, if desired, set in a few
pieces of diet-pack Mandarin oranges. Pour into a mold and
chill until set.

TOTAL CALORIES FOR THE DAY: 594, INCLUDING
59 OF SNACKS

80	*Breakfast*	162	*Lunch*	293	*Dinner*
70	1 scrambled egg with	100	1 small defatted frankfurter	224	Crisp baked chicken*
10	2 chopped mushrooms	15	½ cup sauer-kraut	15	½ cup cauli-flower
	Black coffee	17	Summer squash	36	Carrot coleslaw*
1	Midmorning drink	30	1 medium peach	18	Melon balls in the round*
			Tea with lemon		Black coffee
			Midafternoon drink	58	6 oz. skim milk at bedtime

BREAKFAST: Don't forget to scramble the egg in your Teflon pan.

LUNCH: To defat your frankfurter, boil it and throw away the water. Then you can broil it a little to give it some character.

CRISP BAKED CHICKEN

Serves 2. Calories per serving: 224.

½ broiler-fryer, cut in half
3 Tbs. half-and-half sour
   cream
1 Tbs. lemon juice
¼ tsp. crushed rosemary leaves

⅛ tsp. salt
Dash of pepper
2 tsps. sesame seed
Dash of paprika
Chopped parsley

☞ Heat oven to 375 degrees. Wash and dry chicken. Blend sour cream, lemon juice, rosemary, salt, and pepper. Spread half the mixture on the chicken and place in a shallow oven-proof dish. Bake until tender, about 50 minutes. Brush with the other half of the sour cream mixture. Sprinkle with the sesame seed and bake 10 minutes more. Sprinkle with chopped parsley before serving.

CARROT COLESLAW

Serves 6.   Calories per serving: about 36.

3 cups cabbage, shredded
3 medium carrots, shredded
¾ cup tart garlic dressing
  (below)
Minced parsley

TART GARLIC DRESSING
1 cup buttermilk
1 clove garlic, pressed
¼ tsp. dry mustard
1½ tsps. lemon juice

☞ Mix all ingredients lightly. Cover and chill 30 minutes before serving.

Make this in a bottle. Mix first 3 ingredients with lemon juice, more if you want it. Shake thoroughly. Allow 2 table-spoons per serving, which is worth 11 calories.

MELON BALLS IN THE ROUND

Makes about 8 half-cup servings. Calories per serving: 18.

1 small cantaloupe
2 envelopes unflavored
  gelatin
3½ cups cold water

⅓ cup lemon juice
2 tsps. Sucaryl
Fresh mint sprigs

☞ Make as many cantaloupe balls as you can. Chill fruit. Soften gelatin in ½ cup of the cold water. Put over low heat and stir until gelatin is dissolved. Add the rest of the water and
[*continued*]

lemon juice and Sucaryl. Cover the bottom of a 1-quart mold with part of the gelatin. Chill until firm. Chill the rest of the gelatin until soupy. Add melon balls to prepared mold and add the soupy gelatin. Chill until firm. Unmold on chilled plate and garnish with sprigs of fresh mint.

TOTAL CALORIES FOR THE DAY: 614, INCLUDING 59 OF SNACKS

	Breakfast		*Lunch*		*Dinner*
160		115		280	
28	4 oz. Mott's 5-Fruit Drink	85	1 cup Campbell's clam chowder	198	Shrimp with bacon blankets*
130	Griddle cakes*	30	1 fresh peach Tea with lemon	30	Zucchini and yellow squash*
2	Diet maple syrup Black coffee		Midafternoon drink	15	Mixed green salad
1	Midmorning drink			37	½ cup pitted fresh cherries Black coffee
				58	6 oz. skim milk at bedtime

GRIDDLE CAKES

Makes 10 to 12 cakes. Calories per 3-cake serving: 120.

    1 egg, beaten   ¾ cup skim milk
¾ cup Diet-mix gluten flour

☞ Put the beaten egg into a measuring cup and add enough milk to fill ¾ cup. Stir into this ¾ measured cup of Diet-mix gluten flour. Beat until smooth, then drop by spoonfuls onto Teflon pan. Turn when first side is brown. How long is it since you've had griddle cakes? The diet syrup tastes the same, it just has a thinner consistency.

SHRIMP WITH BACON BLANKETS

Serves 2. Calories per serving: 198.

12 shrimp, fresh or frozen	⅛ tsp. powdered thyme
1 Tbs. lemon juice	6 slices bacon cut in half
1 Tbs. water	crosswise
1 Tbs. dill weed	

☞ If you are using fresh shrimp, shell and devein them. Place the raw shrimp in a 8-inch pie plate. Mix lemon juice, water, dill, and thyme. Drizzle over the shrimp. Turn to coat well. Let marinate half an hour at least. Wrap each shrimp in bacon, fastening with toothpicks. Arrange the shrimp on broiler pan and broil 3 inches from heat about 5 or 6 minutes, turning occasionally to crisp bacon on all sides. Drain on a paper towel.

ZUCCHINI AND YELLOW SQUASH

☞ Slice a small yellow squash and a zucchini with an onion. Place in saucepan with just a little water. Cook until the vegetables are crisply tender. Sprinkle with freshly ground pepper and salt.

TOTAL CALORIES FOR THE DAY: 652, INCLUDING
59 OF SNACKS

97	*Breakfast*	230	*Lunch*	266	*Dinner*
25	½ cup V-8 juice	150	Salmon soufflé*	148	Calves' liver
50	½ cup Irish oatmeal	15	Watercress salad	23	Spinach
22	2 oz. skim milk	65	Whole orange	15	Squash
	Black coffee		Tea with lemon	20	Coleslaw
				60	Apricot mousse*
1	Midmorning drink		Midafternoon tea		Black coffee
				58	6 oz. skim milk at bedtime

SALMON SOUFFLÉ

Serves 3.   Calories per serving: 150.

3 eggs, separated
1 can diet cream of mushroom
   soup
1 tsp. dill

1 cup cooked or canned
   salmon
Dash pepper
Salt to taste

☞ Beat the yolks and stir into the soup. Add the dill, salmon, salt, and pepper. Beat the egg whites until stiff but not dry. Fold into the salmon and soup mixture. Pour into an ungreased soufflé dish and bake in a 350-degree oven for 45 minutes. Serve immediately.

Brush the calves' liver with low-calorie Italian dressing and sauté it briefly in the Teflon pan.

APRICOT MOUSSE

Serves 6.   Calories per serving: 60.

☞ Drain 1 #2 can of water-packed apricots and add water to the juice to make 2 cups. Press apricots through sieve or place in blender. Heat half the liquid and dissolve 2 packages lemon D-Zerta in it. Add the rest of the liquid and the apricot pulp. Chill until slightly thickened. In a mixing bowl, sprinkle ⅓ cup non-fat dry milk over ¼ cup water. Add 1 teaspoon lemon juice. Beat until stiff. Fold into apricot mixture. Pour into 1-quart mold and chill until firm.

TOTAL CALORIES FOR THE DAY: 594, INCLUDING
59 OF SNACKS

	85 Breakfast		145 Lunch		305 Dinner
50	Piece of melon	100	Clam chowder	190	Fish filets with
35	1 slice of gluten		(page 67)		egg sauce*
	toast	45	½ cup diet	30	Stewed
	Black coffee		apricots		tomatoes
			Tea with lemon	20	Swiss chard
1	Midmorning			15	Mixed green
	snack		Midafternoon		salad
			drink	50	½ grapefruit
					Black coffee
				58	6 oz. skim milk
					at bedtime

FISH FILETS WITH EGG SAUCE

Serves 4.   Calories per serving: 190.

1 pkg. flounder filets,
   partially thawed
1 egg, beaten
   Fine cracker crumbs
2 large onion slices
½ cup milk
2 tsps. butter
⅛ tsp. paprika

1 can diet cream of
   mushroom soup
2 hard-boiled eggs, finely
   chopped
2 Tbs. green pepper, finely
   chopped
¼ cup milk
⅛ tsp. pepper

☞ Dip the fish in beaten egg and then in the cracker
crumbs. Shake off as many crumbs as possible. Place in a lightly
oiled baking dish. Arrange the onion rings over the fish. Top
with milk and dot with butter. Sprinkle fish with paprika and

bake in a moderate oven (350 degrees) about 30 minutes, or until fish flakes easily. Meanwhile, combine the other ingredients. Cook and stir over medium heat until thoroughly blended and heated. Spoon sauce over filets.

TOTAL CALORIES FOR THE DAY: 624, INCLUDING 59 OF SNACKS

72	Breakfast	64	Lunch	429	Dinner
50	½ cup Post Toasties	55	½ cup Campbell's chicken soup with rice	332	½ broiled chicken Kyoto*
22	2 oz. skim milk Black coffee	9	Lime D-Zerta Tea with lemon	32	Cabbage and celery*
1	Midmorning snack		Midafternoon tea	15	Cucumber salad
				50	Fresh pineapple spears Black coffee
				58	6 oz. skim milk at bedtime

BROILED CHICKEN KYOTO

Serves 2.   Calories per serving: 332.

> 1 medium broiler, split   1 tsp. rosemary
> ⅔ cup soy sauce   Salt, pepper, and MSG
> ½ cup tomato ketchup

☞ Combine ingredients and marinate chicken in sauce 1 hour or more. Barbecue over charcoal or in the oven, basting several times with the marinade.

[continued]

CABBAGE AND CELERY

Serves 2.   Calories per serving: 32.

1 cup cabbage, shredded   Boiling water to cover
1 cup celery, shredded   Salt and MSG

☞ Pour boiling water over the shredded vegetables and cook for 5 minutes, so they are still crisp. Season. Won't give you indigestion this way, either.

TOTAL CALORIES FOR THE DAY: 636, INCLUDING 59 OF SNACKS

97 *Breakfast*	175 *Lunch*	305 *Dinner*
25 ½ cup tomato juice	125 Shrimp gumbo*	230 Lamb on rotisserie*
50 ½ cup diet Wheat Puffs	15 Tossed green salad	15 Fresh asparagus
22 2 oz. skim milk Black coffee	35 Snow pudding* Tea with lemon	25 Louise's hot and cold carrots*
1 Midmorning drink	Midafternoon drink	35 Spiced fruit compote (page 26)
		58 6 oz. skim milk at bedtime

SHRIMP GUMBO

Serves 6. Calories per serving: 125. Can be frozen.

2 slices bacon, chopped	½ tsp. pepper
3 onions, diced	2 tsps. garlic powder
1 pkg. frozen okra	½ tsp. thyme
5 cups water	1 lb. uncooked shrimp,
1 cup canned tomatoes	shelled and cleaned
½ cup celery, chopped	3 Tbs. chopped parsley
1 green pepper, chopped	1 cup cooked rice
Salt	

☞ Cook the bacon in a saucepan until nearly crisp. Drain the fat. Add the onions and okra and sauté for 5 minutes, stirring frequently. Stir in the water, tomatoes, celery, green pepper, salt, pepper, garlic powder, and thyme. Cook over low heat for 30 minutes. Add the shrimp. Cook for 10 minutes. Serve with the rice. I admit that 1 cup of rice isn't much for 6 people, so if you are having guests, cook more rice. You are supposed to have ⅙ of a cup. Sorry about that.

SNOW PUDDING

Serves 6. Calories per serving: 35.

2 Tbs. gelatin	¾ cup lemon juice
¼ cup cold water	1 tsp. lemon rind, grated
2¾ cups boiling water	Dash salt
2 Tbs. sugar	2 egg whites, beaten
2 Tbs. Sucaryl	

☞ Soften the gelatin in the cold water. Add the boiling water and stir until dissolved. Stir in the Sucaryl, lemon juice, grated rind, and salt. Chill until mixture begins to set, then

[continued]

beat with a rotary beater until frothy. Fold in the stiffly beaten egg whites. Chill in a mold or in 6 individual molds.

LAMB ON ROTISSERIE

3 ounces: 230 calories.

☞ Have your butcher bone and roll a leg of lamb. Cut it in 3 parts, ⅓ cut up in 1½-inch squares to make stew with, ⅓ cut in 1½-inch squares to make shish kebab with, some other week. Put those in the freezer. The best-looking third (from the middle) put on your rotisserie after seasoning well with salt, pepper, monosodium glutamate and marjoram and garlic. It is easy to slice this thin with your electric knife if you have one. If not, slice as people always have.

LOUISE'S HOT AND COLD CARROTS

This is really a salad-type thing.

1 can S. S. Pierce whole carrots	3 drops Tabasco
1 cup tarragon vinegar	Salt and pepper
2 garlic cloves	Parsley, chopped

☞ Drain carrots well. Heat other ingredients and add carrots. Chill well. Sprinkle with finely chopped parsley before serving.

TOTAL CALORIES FOR THE DAY: 513, INCLUDING
59 OF SNACKS

115	*Breakfast*	
80	Double-boiler scrambled egg*	
35	Served on 1 slice gluten toast Black coffee	
1	Midmorning drink	

109	*Lunch*	
100	2 oz. cottage cheese mixed with chopped radishes, onion, green pepper, on 1 slice Hollywood dark diet bread	
9	Raspberry D-Zerta Tea with lemon Midafternoon snack	

230	*Dinner*	
125	Shrimp Gumbo (page 273)	
30	Jellied vegetable salad	
75	Strawberries with red wine Black coffee	
58	6 oz. skim milk at bedtime	

DOUBLE-BOILER SCRAMBLED EGG

Serves 1.

☞ Add a tablespoon of milk to 1 egg and place in top of a double boiler. Cook until it reaches the desired consistency. Flavor with salt, pepper, and monosodium glutamate.

TOTAL CALORIES FOR THE DAY: 612, INCLUDING
59 OF SNACKS

47 *Breakfast*	116 *Lunch*	390 *Dinner*
12 ½ cup diet cranberry juice	0 Meat soup stock	335 Meatballs with mushroom sauce*
35 1 slice gluten toast	71 Cold vegetable plate* vinaigrette on lettuce	20 Broccoli
Black coffee		15 Mixed green salad
1 Midmorning drink	45 Butterscotch pudding	20 Rhubarb compote
	Tea with lemon	Black coffee
	Midafternoon drink	58 6 oz. skim milk at bedtime

☞ Time to run up some more meat soup stock. Recipe on Page 54.

COLD VEGETABLE PLATE

☞ This is the time to use up all those odds and ends. Cold asparagus spears, some of Louise's carrots, a couple of sliced pickled beets, green beans, all with a good lemony spiced dressing of Italian diet salad dressing.

MEATBALLS WITH MUSHROOM SAUCE

Serves 6.   Calories per serving: 335.

1¼ lbs. ground lean beef	2 tsps. salt
1 onion, grated	¼ tsp. pepper

1 Tbs. MSG	1 lb. mushrooms, sliced
3 Tbs. cold water	2 egg yolks
1 egg, beaten	2 Tbs. lemon juice
1 Tbs. butter	2 Tbs. chopped parsley

☞ Mix the beef, onion, 1 teaspoon salt, pepper, MSG, water, and egg. Shape into 1-inch balls. Do you know the trick of dipping your hands in cold water to keep them from sticking? Melt the butter in the Teflon pan and brown the meatballs. Remove and keep warm on a paper-towel-lined pan. Sauté the sliced mushrooms in the fat remaining in the skillet. Beat the egg yolks, lemon juice, and the other teaspoon salt together and add to the mushrooms, stirring constantly to prevent curdling. Add the meatballs and the parsley. Cook over low heat for 5 minutes; do not let boil.

TOTAL CALORIES FOR THE DAY: 625, INCLUDING 59 OF SNACKS

82 *Breakfast*	175 *Lunch*	309 *Dinner*
12 ½ cup diet cranberry juice	100 Frankfurter	208 Steak teriyaki*
	30 Sauerkraut	21 ½ cup white turnips
70 1 soft-boiled egg	45 Diet peaches	
Black coffee	Tea with lemon	30 Sliced tomato
		50 Honeydew melon
1 Midmorning snack	Midafternoon drink	Black coffee
		58 6 oz. skim milk at bedtime

STEAK TERIYAKI

Two pieces, 1″ by 4″ by 1″: 208 calories. The marinade will do more than the 2 pieces. This is just so you'll know how much you can have.

2 T-bone steaks, 1-inch thick	1 clove chopped garlic
½ cup soy sauce	2 Tbs. Sucaryl
¼ cup white wine	½ tsp. powdered ginger

 Combine all ingredients and marinate steak in sauce for 15 minutes. Broil or barbecue until desired degree of rareness is obtained. Baste a few times while cooking.

TOTAL CALORIES FOR THE DAY: 608, INCLUDING
59 OF SNACKS

163	*Breakfast*	92	*Lunch*	294	*Dinner*
28	Mott's 5-Fruit Drink	60	Mulligatawney (page 16)	270	Lamb Stew*
100	2 slices crisp bacon	32	Apricot whip (page 109)	15	Mixed green salad
35	1 slice gluten toast		Tea with lemon	9	Lime D-Zerta
	Black coffee				Black coffee
			Midafternoon broth	58	6 oz. skim milk before bedtime
1	Midmorning drink				

LAMB STEW NO. 3 (Lamb, Limas and Tomatoes)

Serves 4. Calories per serving: 270.

1 pkg. frozen green lima beans
1 Tbs. cooking oil
2 medium onions, peeled and minced
1 clove garlic, minced
1 lb. cubed lean boneless lamb

1 cup canned tomatoes, drained and minced
1 tsp. salt
Pepper to taste
¼ tsp. cinnamon

☞ Cook beans according to directions on box and drain part of the water. Heat the oil in the Teflon pan and sauté the onions and lamb over low heat for 10 minutes. Combine tomatoes with lamb, onions, and beans. Add salt, pepper, and cinnamon and mix. Bake in a casserole in a 350-degree oven for 25 minutes, or until lamb is tender.

TOTAL CALORIES FOR THE DAY: 709, INCLUDING
59 OF SNACKS

	Breakfast		*Lunch*		*Dinner*
112	**Breakfast**	120	**Lunch**	418	**Dinner**
42	½ cup blue-berries on	100	Shrimp in aspic (page 231)	250	Pepper steak*
50	½ cup Special K	20	1 cup rhubarb Tea with lemon	100	½ cup rice
22	2 oz. skim milk Black coffee		Midafternoon tea	58	Orange-pineapple sherbet (page 257)
1	Midmorning drink				Black coffee
				58	6 oz. skim milk at bedtime

PEPPER STEAK

Serves 3.   Calories per serving: 250.

1 onion, sliced from the top	9 oz. round steak or filet, cut
1 Tbs. vegetable oil	in thin, thin pieces
1½ cups strong bouillon	3 green peppers, cut in
1 Tbs. Chinese molasses	1-inch squares
1½ Tbs. cornstarch	

☞ Sauté the onion in 1 tablespoon oil in the Teflon pan. Add the bouillon (use Bovril) the Chinese molasses, and the cornstarch which has been mixed with cold water to form a paste. Cook until shiny and thickened. Add thin, thin slices of beef and green peppers. Season with soy sauce.

TOTAL CALORIES FOR THE DAY: 580, INCLUDING
1 OF SNACK

68	*Breakfast*	151	*Lunch*	360	*Dinner*
12	½ cup cranberry juice	70	Gazpacho (page 188)	300	Corned beef and cabbage
45	½ cup Special K cereal with 2 oz. skim milk	25	Garlic croutons	25	Sliced cucumber with dill weed and 1 Tbs. yogurt
		55	1 medium orange		
			Tea with lemon		
11	Coffee with Coffee-mate		Midafternoon tea	35	Snow pudding (page 95)
1	Diet drink in midmorning				Black coffee

TOTAL CALORIES FOR THE DAY: 621, INCLUDING
31 OF SNACKS

28	Breakfast	205	Lunch	357	Dinner
28	Mott's 5-Fruit Drink	149	Crab bouquet salad*	250	Veal chop en casserole*
	Black coffee	21	Ry-Krisp	10	Fresh cucumbers in dill
1	Midmorning drink	35	1 fresh peach	97	Angel lime pie*
			Tea with lemon		Black coffee
			Midafternoon drink	30	Coffee shake at bedtime

CRAB BOUQUET SALAD

Serves 3.   Calories per serving: 149.

    1 7-oz. can crabmeat   1 head of Boston lettuce,
    ½ cup celery, chopped   washed and separated
    ¼ cup sweet pickles, chopped   into leaves
    2 Tbs. bottled low-calorie   2 hard-boiled eggs, shelled
       Italian dressing

☞ Drain crabmeat and carefully remove any of that miserable bony tissue. Mix crab with celery and pickles in a bowl. Pour dressing over and toss lightly. Chill well. When ready to serve, form lettuce leaves into cups in individual salad bowls. Green glass ones look very cool. Mound salad becomingly in centers. Cut eggs in quarters lengthwise, scoop out yolks. Cut each white into thin strips and arrange petal-fashion over salads. Press yolks through a sieve into center (like a daisy, get it?) Stick a skewer threaded with celery pieces and one stuffed olive in on an angle.

VEAL CHOP EN CASSEROLE

Serves 1.   Calories: 250.

Trace of oil	5 medium mushrooms, sliced
1 trimmed veal chop	3 oz. white wine
Trace of flour	½ fresh tomato, cubed
6 pearl onions	Salt, pepper, and paprika

☞ Brush the bottom of an earthenware casserole with a little oil. Dip a trimmed (fat and skin removed) chop in flour, then knock the flour off. Place chop in casserole. Bake in a 375-degree oven until the chop is golden brown. To this add 6 pearl onions, sliced mushrooms, white wine, and tomato and simmer in the oven for about 25 minutes. Baste the chop a few times. Sprinkle with chopped truffles (if you have any) or finely chopped parsley. Serve right from casserole.

ANGEL LIME PIE

*Serves 8.   Calories per serving (That's a 1-inch serving, sister!):
97.*

6 Tbs. zwieback crumbs (about 5 slices)	2 Tbs. granulated sugar
	1 cup hot water
2 tsps. brown sugar	½ cup instant dry non-fat
¼ tsp. cinnamon	milk
2 Tbs. butter, melted	½ cup ice water
2 pkg. low-calorie lime gelatin	1 Tbs. lemon juice

☞ Mix zwieback crumbs with brown sugar and cinnamon in a small bowl. Blend in melted butter. Press evenly over bottom and sides of an 8-inch pie plate. Bake in a 350-degree oven 10 minutes; cool completely on a wire rack. Dissolve gelatin and granulated sugar in hot water in a small bowl. Chill about

[continued]

1 hour or until as thick as unbeaten egg white. Sprinkle non-fat milk powder over ice water in a chilled large bowl. Beat with an electric beater at high speed 3 minutes or until soft peaks form. Add lemon juice, continue beating until mixture stands in firm peaks. Fold into thickened gelatin mixture. Spoon into cooled crust, chill until firm. Garnish with a few seedless grapes. Cut into 8 pieces.

TOTAL CALORIES FOR THE DAY: 667, INCLUDING
59 OF SNACKS

75	*Breakfast*	230	*Lunch*	303	*Dinner*
75	1 scrambled egg Black coffee	165	Open-face grilled cheese sandwich* with	220	Poulet au pot*
1	Midmorning snack			20	Perfection salad
		10	Watercress garnish	63	Iced fruit* Black coffee
		55	½ cup fresh pineapple Tea with lemon Midafternoon tea	58	6 oz. skim milk at bedtime

---

OPEN-FACE GRILLED CHEESE SANDWICH

This is a snare and a delusion, as are most of the delicious-sounding things that you have been longing for. Have 1 slice of bread with 1 ounce of cheese—your choice, Swiss, American, processed, whatever—but only 1 ounce. Use some mustard to spice it up.

POULET AU POT

Serves 2. Calories per serving: 220. ■ *The dog days are upon us. If they are not, then have the chicken hot. If it turns out one of those days when the humidity and the thermometer all rise sky-high, do the chicken in the morning, cool it, and use*

[*continued*]

the broth to make a clear chicken gelatin. Bone the chicken,
add some of the cooked vegetables, and make a mold.

1 whole 3-lb. chicken	Pepper
Carrots	Bag leaf
Celery	Pinch of saffron
Salt	Leeks

☞ Make a bouquet garni of large pieces of carrot, celery, and leeks. Place in cold water and boil for about 20 minutes. Into this broth place 1 whole 3-lb. chicken and cook for ½ hour, or until done. Add salt, pepper, bay leaf, and a pinch of saffron. Remove the vegetables from the pot, cut into smaller pieces. Arrange in soup plates. Cut chicken into small portions; strain the broth over the vegetables and chicken, and serve. If it is hot, soak a package of plain gelatin in a little cold water, put 2 cups of the hot strained defatted chicken broth in the soaked gelatin. Stir until dissolved. Arrange chicken and vegetables in a mold; pour over gelatin mixture and chill until firm.

ICED FRUIT

Serves 4.   Calories per serving: 63.

1 can diet pack pineapple tidbits	1 can diet pack Mandarin oranges
⅛ tsp. ground ginger	12 purple grapes

☞ Drain syrup from pineapple tidbits into a cup. Stir in ginger. Drain Mandarin orange segments. Crush a tray of ice cubes fine. Pile into cone shape on a serving tray. Place a small cup on top. Fill with pineapple-ginger syrup. Arrange pineapple tidbits, Mandarin orange segments, and grapes in rows on ice cone. Serve with wooden picks to spear fruits and dip into the sauce.

TOTAL CALORIES FOR THE DAY: 633, INCLUDING 59 OF SNACKS

105	*Breakfast*	190	*Lunch*	279	*Dinner*
70	Poached egg on	50	Watercress	210	Sweet and sour
35	1 slice gluten		soup*		tongue*
	toast	110	Salad plate:	25	Spinach en
	Black coffee		6 medium		branche
			shrimp	19	Raw zucchini
1	Midmorning		½ cup		salad*
	drink		cooked	25	Jewel parfaits*
			cold		Black coffee
			broccoli		
			Lemon	58	6 oz. skim milk
			wedges		at bedtime
			Lettuce		
		30	Small bunch		
			Thompson		
			seedless		
			grapes		
			Tea with lemon		
			Midafternoon		
			drink		

WATERCRESS SOUP

Serves 6. Calories per serving: 50.

1 bunch watercress	1 tsp. instant minced onion
1 Tbs. flour	1 tsp. salt
3 cups skim milk	

[*continued*]

☞ Wash watercress and dry. Set aside 6 sprigs for garnish, then chop remaining stems and leaves. There should be about 1¾ cups. Smooth flour and 1 to 2 tablespoons skim milk to a paste in a medium-size saucepan. Stir in remaining milk, onion, and salt. Cook, stirring constantly, until mixture thickens and boils, 1 minute. Remove from heat. Stir in watercress. Ladle into heated soup bowls and serve at once, garnished with watercress.

SWEET AND SOUR TONGUE

Serves 6.   Calories per serving: 210. ■ *This can be made several days in advance and also freezes well.*

4 ginger snaps
¼ cup brown sugar plus 1 scant tsp. Sucaryl
¼ cup white vinegar
1 cup hot water
¼ tsp. salt
1 lemon, sliced paper thin
1 lb. cooked tongue, sliced thin

☞ Combine the first 6 ingredients in a saucepan and bring to a boil. Lower the flame and let simmer 10 minutes. When the consistency is as thick as you want it, remove from the heat and pour over the tongue.

RAW ZUCCHINI SALAD

☞ Slice raw zucchini lengthwise in ⅛-inch thickness, about 1½ inches long. Marinate in lemon juice, pepper, and salt.

JEWEL PARFAITS

Serves 6.   Calories per serving: 25.

2 envelopes unflavored gelatin   1 Tbs. lemon juice

1 bottle (16 oz.) cherry flavor   flavor no-calorie drink
     no-calorie drink   Green food coloring
1 bottle (16 oz.) lemon-lime   1 medium banana

☞ Soften 1 envelope of the unflavored gelatin in ½ cup of the cherry drink in a small saucepan. Heat over low heat, stirring constantly, just until gelatin dissolves. Remove from heat. Stir in remaining cherry drink. Soften the remaining envelope gelatin in ½ cup of the lemon-lime drink in a second small saucepan. Heat over low heat, stirring constantly, just until gelatin dissolves. Stir in remaining drink, green coloring, and lemon juice. Chill both mixtures 50 minutes, until thick as unbeaten egg white, then keep at room temperature while layering in parfait glasses. Spoon ¼ cup thickened cherry gelatin into each of 3 glasses, start lemon-lime in another 3. Put a thin slice of banana between each layer of color, chilling to firm each layer. Garnish with banana slices.

TOTAL CALORIES FOR THE DAY: 623½,
INCLUDING 59 OF SNACKS

66	*Breakfast*	170½	*Lunch*	328	*Dinner*
31	2 oz. cranberry juice with 2 oz. orange juice	12½	Borscht (page 12)	225	Eastern Mediterranean beefburgers*
35	1 slice gluten toast	100	4 sardines on lettuce with lemon wedges	25	½ cup broccoli
	Black coffee			15	Mixed green salad
1	Midmorning drink	58	Fresh fruit plate: 1 peach 1 apricot 6 cherries	63	Cardamon cup soufflé*
			Tea with lemon		Black coffee
			Midafter-noon drink	58	6 oz. skim milk at bedtime

EASTERN MEDITERRANEAN BEEFBURGERS

Serves 4.   Calories per serving: 225.

1 Tbs. cooking oil
4 1-inch slices unpeeled
   eggplant
   Salt, pepper and garlic salt
   to taste, 1 tsp. MSG
¾ lb. very lean ground beef
1 very small onion, minced

1 egg
1 Tbs. soy sauce
1 slice bread, soaked in water
   and lightly squeezed
1 large tomato cut in 4 slices
¼ cup parsley, finely chopped

☞ Heat the oil in a very large skillet (must hold the 4 eggplant slices). Sprinkle the slices lightly with salt, pepper, garlic salt, and MSG. Sauté on both sides until almost tender. Combine the meat, onion, egg, soy sauce, bread, more salt and pepper; mix by hand. Divide into 4 parts and cover each eggplant slice. Cover the meat with a tomato slice and chopped parsley. Place in a preheated broiler 3 inches below the flames for 10 minutes or until meat is the desired taste of doneness.

CARDAMOM CUP SOUFFLÉ

Serves 4. Calories per serving: 63.

⅛ cup sugar	⅛ tsp. ground cardamom
2 eggs, separated	½ tsp. grated lemon rind
¼ tsp. baking powder	1½ Tbs. lemon juice
⅛ tsp. salt	

☞ Butter 4 half-cup soufflé dishes. Make a 2″ standup collar with a piece of foil 6″ wide and 11″ long, folded in half lengthwise. Butter lightly and wrap around each soufflé dish. overlapping ends. Fasten with a paper clip. Sprinkle cups and collars lightly with about 1 tablespoon of the sugar, tapping out any excess. Beat in a medium-size bowl egg whites with the baking powder, salt, and cardamom just until they form soft peaks. Beat egg yolks well in large bowl; beat in remaining sugar, 1 tablespoon at a time, until very thick; then stir in lemon rind and juice. Fold in beaten egg white mixture. Spoon into prepared dishes, dividing evenly. Set cups, not touching, in a shallow baking pan. Place on oven shelf. Pour boiling water into pan to depth of 1″. Bake in a 325-degree oven for 30 minutes until puffy and firm in center. Carefully peel off collars and serve at once.

TOTAL CALORIES FOR THE DAY: 624, INCLUDING
59 OF SNACKS

63	*Breakfast*	157	*Lunch*	345	*Dinner*
28	½ cup Mott's 5-Fruit Drink	100	3 broiled chicken livers	265	Shish kebab*
35	1 slice gluten toast	15	½ cup stewed tomatoes	30	Artichoke hearts on watercress
	Black coffee	15	Coleslaw	50	Cinnamon pears*
1	Midmorning drink	27	½ cup fresh strawberries		Black coffee
			Tea with lemon	58	6 oz. skim milk at bedtime
			Afternoon refreshment		

SHISH KEBAB

Serves 3.   Calories per serving: 265.

1 lb. lamb from leg, all visible fat removed
½ Tbs. olive oil
Juice of ½ lemon
Salt, pepper, and MSG
½ medium onion, peeled and sliced

2 bay leaves
Fresh mushrooms
1 can small cooked onions
Green pepper, cut in 1-inch squares
Cherry tomatoes

☞ Cut the meat into 1-inch cubes. Mix olive oil and lemon juice and rub into meat. Place in a dish, sprinkle with salt, pepper, monosodium glutamate, slices of onion, and bay leaves. Marinate for 3 or 4 hours or overnight. Arrange meat on skewers, alternating with whole mushrooms, canned onions, green pepper squares, and cherry tomatoes. Broil until meat is well browned, turning several times.

CINNAMON PEARS

Serves 4.   Calories per serving: 50.

2 medium-size firm ripe pears
½ cup water
1 tsp. Sucaryl

1 2-inch piece of stick
cinnamon

☞ Pare the pears, then halve and core. Place cut side down in large frying pan. Add the rest of the ingredients; cover pan. Heat to boiling point, then simmer until pears are tender. Spoon into serving dishes, ½ pear per person. Serve either warm or chilled.

TOTAL CALORIES FOR THE DAY: 616, INCLUDING
59 OF SNACKS

12	*Breakfast*	105	*Lunch*	440	*Dinner*
12	½ cup diet cranberry juice	15	Cold jellied chicken consommé	325	Brown lamb stew with dumplings*
	Black coffee	40	Fresh asparagus salad*	15	Green salad
1	Midmorning snack	50	½ cantaloupe Tea with lemon	100	Bananas and oranges with rum*
			Midafternoon break		Black coffee
				58	6 oz. skim milk at bedtime

FRESH ASPARAGUS SALAD

Serves 3.   Calories per serving: 40.

Iceberg lettuce, broken
   in small pieces
Diet Italian dressing
1 lb. fresh asparagus, cooked
2 sliced tomatoes

1 small cucumber, peeled and
   sliced
3 scallions, sliced thin
1 hard-boiled egg, sliced
¼ cup sliced ripe olives

☞ Toss the lettuce with a little dressing and spread it out in a wide bowl or deep plate. Put little bunches of 3 or 4 asparagus spears all around the outside with groups of 3 or 4 slices of tomato between. Insert the cucumber slices over and between the asparagus and tomatoes. Sprinkle the sliced scallions over everything. Arrange the egg slices in a small circle on the center of the plate and put the ripe olives over the eggs. Drizzle Italian dressing lightly over the whole thing.

BROWN LAMB STEW
WITH DUMPLINGS

Serves 6. Calories per serving: 325. Can be frozen. ■ *Here is where you get out that piece of frozen leg of lamb that you squirreled away awhile back. Cut the meat neatly into 1-inch pieces, removing every speck of fat.*

About 2 lbs. boneless lamb	1 tsp. salt
9 small white onions	1 cup water
1 clove garlic, pressed	1 cup sliced carrots
1 bay leaf	1 cup green peas

☞ Brown the meat in your Teflon pan. After the meat has browned, add onions, garlic, bay leaf, salt, and water. Cover. Heat to boiling. Simmer 45 minutes. Add carrots. Simmer 15 minutes longer. While the carrots are cooking, make the dumplings. Add peas to kettle. Heat to boiling again. Drop the dumplings in 3 mounds on top of hot stew. Steam 20 minutes, or until dumplings are puffy and light.

DUMPLINGS: Combine ½ cup sifted regular flour, ½ teaspoon baking powder, ¼ teaspoon salt, and ¼ teaspoon nutmeg in a small bowl. Add ¼ cup skim milk all at once and stir just until flour is evenly moist. Remove dumplings to a heated serving platter. Remove bay leaf from stew and put stew in center of platter.

BANANAS AND ORANGES WITH RUM

Serves 4. Calories per serving: 100.

4 bananas, peeled and split	Sprinkle of brown sugar
1½ unpeeled oranges, sliced very thin	¼ cup melted butter
	¼ cup warm rum

[continued]

☞ Arrange the bananas close together in a shallow casserole and lay the oranges over them, overlapping a little. Sprinkle with brown sugar and melted butter. Bake 15 min. in a slow oven (300 degrees); remove from oven. Pour the warm rum over the bananas and serve flaming.

TOTAL CALORIES FOR THE DAY: 635, INCLUDING 59 OF SNACKS

	Breakfast		Lunch		Dinner
37	*Breakfast*	190	*Lunch*	359	*Dinner*
37	2 oz. diet cranberry juice mixed with 2 oz. orange juice Black coffee	15	Cold consommé	247	Fish filets*
		20	Asparagus vinaigrette	55	Baked tomatoes
		85	1 oz. Camembert cheese	15	Spinach
		70	1 Golden Delicious apple	15	Mixed green salad
1	Midmorning drink		Tea with lemon	37	½ cup grapefruit sections Black coffee
			Midafternoon tea	58	6 oz. skim milk at bedtime

FISH FILETS

Serves 2.   Calories per serving: 247.

2 filets of sole, about 6 oz. each
1 Tbs. lemon juice
2 Tbs. low-calorie mayonnaise
1 scallion, including green top, thinly sliced

1 tsp. dried parsley flakes
⅛ tsp. salt
Dash of pepper
2 Tbs. slivered blanched almonds

☞ Heat broiler. Wipe filets dry with a paper towel. In a small bowl, combine the lemon juice, mayonnaise, scallion, parsley flakes, salt and pepper. Arrange the filets on the broiler pan. Spread with the mayonnaise mixture. Broil 5 inches from the heat 5 or 6 minutes or until fish begins to brown and flake when tested with a fork. Sprinkle with almonds and continue to broil until the almonds are lightly browned. This should take about 2 minutes. Sprinkle with paprika and serve with lemon wedges.

TOTAL CALORIES FOR THE DAY: 573, INCLUDING
1 OF SNACKS

31 *Breakfast*	201 *Lunch*	340 *Dinner*
31 2 oz. diet cranberry juice mixed with 2 oz. orange juice Black coffee	116 Baked eggs in crispy nests*	256 Hamburger ring* with
	30 Sliced tomato	10 Mushrooms
	55 1 chocolate brownie*	12 Green beans
	Tea with lemon	12 Salad
1 Midmorning drink	Midafternoon tea	50 Fresh fruit cup Black coffee
		Drink No-Cal something tonight. We were profligate today with that brownie, don't you know?

BAKED EGGS IN CRISPY NESTS

Serves 4.   Calories per serving: 116.

1¼ cups cornflakes	Dash of crushed rosemary
1 tsp. melted butter	Sprig of watercress or
4 eggs	parsley
¼ tsp. salt	

☞ Mix the cornflakes with the melted butter and toss lightly. Place mixture in 4 greased custard cups and press down in center with the back of a spoon. Slip 1 egg carefully into each nest. Sprinkle with salt and rosemary. Bake in a slow oven (325 degrees) 20 minutes or until eggs are set. To serve, loosen nests with spatula and lift out gently onto serving plates. Garnish with sprig of watercress or parsley.

CHOCOLATE BROWNIE

Makes 32. Calories per piece: 55.   ■   *Can be frozen.*

1 square unsweetened chocolate	2 eggs, beaten
⅓ cup butter	1 cup flour, sifted very fine
2 Tbs. Sucaryl	½ tsp. salt
2 tsps. vanilla	½ tsp. baking soda
	⅔ cup chopped walnuts

☞ Melt the unsweetened chocolate and butter in a saucepan over low heat. Remove from heat. Add Sucaryl, vanilla, and beaten eggs. Stir until well blended. Add sifted cake flour, salt, and baking soda. Mix until blended. Stir in the chopped walnuts. Pour into a greased 8-inch-square pan. Level batter in pan. Bake in a slow oven (325 degrees) for 20 minutes. Cool. Cut into 32 pieces. Yes, they are small, but what do you expect?

HAMBURGER RING WITH MUSHROOMS

Serves 6.   Calories per serving: 256.

1½ lbs. ground lean beef	1 tsp. Worcestershire sauce
2 eggs, beaten	1½ tsps. salt
¾ cup skim milk	½ tsp. paprika
2 Tbs. minced onion	

☞ Blend all the ingredients well and pack into a small greased ring mold. Bake 1 hour in a 350-degree oven and turn out on a heated platter. Sauté 1 pound sliced mushrooms in the Teflon pan and use them to fill the middle.

TOTAL CALORIES FOR THE DAY: 620, INCLUDING
58 OF SNACKS

105	*Breakfast*	100	*Lunch*	357	*Dinner*
70	Poached egg on	100	½ cup cottage	320	Pork tenderloin
35	1 slice gluten		cheese with		stuffed with
	bread		assorted fruit		prunes*
	Black coffee		salad	12	Green beans
			Tea with lemon	15	Mixed green
	Midmorning				salad
	drink		Midafternoon	10	Mocha gelatin*
			tea		Black coffee
				58	6 oz. skim milk
					at bedtime

PORK TENDERLOIN
STUFFED WITH PRUNES

Serves 4.   Calories per serving: 320.

1	pork tenderloin, split lengthwise	Flour
12	pitted prunes, stewed and drained	

☞ Flatten out the split tenderloin and rub it with garlic. Put the prunes in and tie the tenderloin up neatly so they won't fall out. Dust lightly with flour. Place on a rack and bake in a 350-degree oven for 30 to 45 minutes per pound. A serving of this is 2 ounces of meat and 3 prunes. Use your little postal scale to weigh the serving. It is more than you think.

MOCHA GELATIN

Serves 4.   Calories per serving: 10.

1 Tbs. gelatin	¾ cup diet canned fruit syrup
¼ cup cold water	
1 cup very hot double-strength coffee	

☞ Soak the gelatin in the cold water and dissolve it in the hot coffee. Add the fruit syrup and pour into a mold that has been dipped in water. Chill 4 hours or more.

TOTAL CALORIES FOR THE DAY: 606, INCLUDING
59 OF SNACKS

105 *Breakfast*	160 *Lunch*	282 *Dinner*
70 1 poached egg on	100 1 defatted frankfurter	100 Broiled lobster
35 1 slice gluten toast	30 1 cup sauer-kraut	20 Broiled mush-rooms
Black coffee	30 1 fresh peach	35 Tomato au gratin (page 77)
1 Midmorning drink	Tea with lemon	77 White Moun-tain radish bowl*
	Midafternoon tea	50 Slice of honey-dew melon
		Black coffee
		58 6 oz. skim milk at bedtime

☞ It's very simple to defat a frankfurter. Just put it in boiling water for 5 minutes and then drain. The fat gets thrown out with the water.

Remember, no butter with the lobster. You can brush it with low-calorie diet salad dressing if you wish.

The same goes for the mushrooms. You can have 4.

WHITE MOUNTAIN RADISH BOWL

Serves 6.   Calories per serving: 77.

6 cups escarole, broken
4 cups radishes, sliced

6 slices bacon, diced
2 Tbs. sugar

2 Tbs. wine vinegar   1 tsp. seasoned salt
2 Tbs. water

☞ Place escarole in a large salad bowl. Mound the radishes on top. Sauté the bacon in a medium-size frying pan. Remove and drain on paper towel. Pour the drippings into a cup and then measure 2 tablespoons back in the pan. Stir in the sugar, wine vinegar, water, and seasoned salt. Heat to boiling. Pour over the radishes in the bowl. Toss lightly to mix.

TOTAL CALORIES FOR THE DAY: 618, INCLUDING
59 OF SNACKS

50	*Breakfast*	147	*Lunch*	362	*Dinner*
50	½ cup diet	100	Chef's salad*	222	Veal
	applesauce	17	1 Ry-Krisp		Parmesan*
	Black coffee	30	Banana	25	Broccoli
1	Midmorning		gelatin*	65	1 ear fresh corn
	drink		Tea with lemon		—NO BUTTER
			Midafternoon	15	Mixed green
			drink		salad
				35	Fresh pine-
					apple
					Black coffee
				58	6 oz. skim milk
					at bedtime

CHEF'S SALAD

Serves 4.   Calories per serving: 100.

⅔ cup mixture of slivered
cooked or canned tongue
or ham, chicken, or
turkey and Swiss cheese
½ Bermuda onion

2 small tomatoes
1 small head chicory
1 bunch watercress
Lettuce to line bowls
8 Tbs. diet French dressing

☞ Cut onion in thin crosswise slices and separate into rings.
Wash tomatoes and cut in wedges. Wash greens, separate, and
tear into bite-size pieces. Combine all ingredients artistically in
bowls and serve with dressing.

BANANA GELATIN

Serves 4.   Calories per serving: 30.

2 pkg. any flavor D-Zerta   1 ripe banana
2 cups boiling water

☞ Dissolve gelatin in 2 cups boiling water. Chill until slightly thickened. Partly fill dessert dishes with gelatin and add slices of banana. Fill mold with remaining gelatin. Chill until firm. Garnish with a slice of banana, berry, or other fruit slice.

VEAL PARMESAN

Serves 4.   Calories per serving: 222.

¾ lb. lean veal cut in 4   3 Tbs. Parmesan cheese
    ½-inch slices   2 tsps. paprika
3 Tbs. butter   Salt and pepper
1 clove garlic, pressed

☞ Pound veal until slices become very thin. Heat butter in Teflon pan; add garlic and then the veal slices. Sprinkle with cheese, paprika, salt and pepper. Cook slowly for 10 or 15 minutes. Turn meat only once during cooking.

TOTAL CALORIES FOR THE DAY: 620, INCLUDING
59 OF SNACKS

47	*Breakfast*	115	*Lunch*	399	*Dinner*
47	½ cup diet cranberry juice	16	Clear onion soup*	250	Spanish chicken*
	Black coffee	56	Sauerkraut salad*	100	½ cup rice
		43	Grape sherbet*	15	½ cup kale
1	Midmorning drink		Tea with lemon	25	Grated carrot salad
			Midafternoon drink	9	Lemon D-Zerta
					Black coffee
				58	6 oz. skim milk at bedtime

CLEAR ONION SOUP

Serves 2. Calories per serving: 16.

> 2 vegetable bouillon tablets　　2 medium onions
> 2 cups boiling water

☞ Dissolve bouillon cubes in boiling water. Slice the onions thinly and add them to the bouillon. Cook until tender.

SAUERKRAUT SALAD

Serves 6. Calories per serving: 56.

> 2½ cups sauerkraut　　　2 Tbs. low-calorie
> 4 radishes　　　　　　　　mayonnaise
> 1 medium green pepper　1 tsp. onion, grated

2 Tbs. half-and-half sour   4 tomatoes
   cream   Few sprigs parsley

☞ Chill can of sauerkraut in refrigerator overnight. Drain off sauerkraut juice. Slice radishes thinly. Cut pepper in thin strips. Combine all ingredients except tomatoes in a large salad bowl. Mix lightly but thoroughly. Cut tomatoes in narrow wedges and place them around the edge of the bowl. Decorate with sprigs of parsley.

GRAPE SHERBET

☞ Put 1 cup crushed ice in the blender with 2 tablespoons frozen grape juice. Whiz.

SPANISH CHICKEN

Serves 4.   Calories per serving: 250.

1 young chicken, cut in pieces   ½ cup capers
2 tomatoes, chopped   1 cup pitted green olives
1 green pepper, chopped   1 pimento, chopped
1 onion, chopped

☞ Place all ingredients in pot with just enough water to cover. Cover pot and simmer for 1½ hours.

TOTAL CALORIES FOR THE DAY: 610, INCLUDING
59 OF SNACKS

25	*Breakfast*	166	*Lunch*	360	*Dinner*
25	½ cup V-8 juice	30	Hot chicken	178	Grilled kidney
	Black coffee		and clam		and bacon*
1	Midmorning		broth	30	Grilled tomato
	drink	100	Silhouette	12	Green beans
			salad*	20	Cucumber and
		36	2 fresh apricots		onion salad
			Tea with lemon	120	Peach pie*
					Black coffee
			Midafternoon		
			tea	58	6 oz. skim milk
					at bedtime

SILHOUETTE SALAD

Serves 4. Calories per serving: 100.

1 envelope unflavored gelatin
1 cup water, divided
1 can diet cream of mush-
   room soup
1 Tbs. lemon juice
   Dash black pepper

1 5-oz. can boned chicken or
   turkey, or leftover
½ cup celery, chopped
¼ cup green pepper, chopped
2 Tbs. pimento, chopped
2 tsps. onion, grated

☞ Sprinkle gelatin on ½ cup cold water to soften. Place over low heat and stir until gelatin is dissolved. Remove from the heat and blend in soup until smooth. Add remaining ½ cup of water, lemon juice, and pepper. Chill to the consistency of unbeaten egg white. Fold in chicken, celery, green pepper, pimento, and onion. Turn into a 3-cup mold and chill untiil firm. Unmold on serving plate garnished with crisp greens.

GRILLED KIDNEY AND BACON

Serves 4.   Calories per serving: 178.

4 lamb kidneys   ½ cup fine cracker crumbs
4 slices bacon   Salt and pepper
1 egg, slightly beaten

☞ Cut kidneys in half and remove tubes. Wrap each piece in half a piece of bacon and fasten with a toothpick. Dip in egg, then in crumbs, and place in baking pan. Bake 20 minutes in hot oven (400 degrees). If you want to, you can use your skewers and have the kidneys *en brochette*.

PEACH PIE

Serves 8.   Calories per serving: 120.

PIE SHELL
¾ cup flour
Pinch nutmeg
Pinch salt
½ stick butter
5 Tbs. ice water

FILLING
4 cups sliced fresh peaches

¼ cup sugar
Pinch salt
½ tsp. cinnamon
¼ tsp. nutmeg
Pinch powdered cloves
⅛ tsp. ginger
2 Tbs. flour
2 tsps. lemon juice
1 Tbs. Sucaryl

☞ Sift flour with nutmeg and salt. Cut the butter in with 2 knives until tiny particles form. Sprinkle cold water, a tablespoon at a time, and press into mixture with a fork. Form into mound of dough and refrigerate to chill. Roll out and fit into 9-inch pie pan. Push dough to sides, leaving center thin. Flute the edges. Prick center with fork.

[continued]

FILLING: Place a layer of peach slices in the unbaked pie shell. Sprinkle with ½ the mixture of the sugar, salt, cinnamon, nutmeg, cloves, ginger, and flour. Mix the lemon juice with the Sucaryl. Sprinkle 1 teaspoon of this over the peaches. Cover with another layer of peaches and repeat the process. Bake in a preheated 425-degree oven for 40 minutes.

TOTAL CALORIES FOR THE DAY: 605, INCLUDING
59 OF SNACKS

70	*Breakfast*	220	*Lunch*	256	*Dinner*
70	1 soft-boiled egg	90	Corn chowder*	175	Oysters en
	Black coffee	30	Sliced tomato		brochette*
1	Midmorning	100	Cherry	12	Spinach
	low-calorie		compote	15	Mixed green
	drink		Tea with lemon		salad
				54	3-inch wedge
			Midafternoon		Casaba
			drink		melon
					Black coffee
				58	6 oz. skim milk
					at bedtime

CORN CHOWDER

Serves 6.   Calories per serving: 90.

1 slice bacon, chopped	½ tsp. paprika
¼ cup onion, chopped	1 bay leaf
½ cup green pepper, diced	1 Tbs. cornstarch
1 potato, pared and diced	1½ cups skim milk
3 cups water	1½ cups corn kernels
¾ tsp. salt	2 Tbs. pimento, chopped
¼ tsp. white pepper	

☞ Cook the bacon until almost crisp. Combine the onion
and green pepper in the pan with the bacon and cook for 5
minutes, stirring frequently. Add the potato, water, salt, pepper, paprika, and bay leaf. Cover and cook over low heat for

[*continued*]

20 minutes. Mix the cornstarch and the milk until smooth and add to the soup, stirring constantly until it comes to a boil. Add the corn and pimentos. Cook 3 minutes.

CHERRY COMPOTE

Serves 6.   Calories per serving: 100.

1 lb. cherries	sweet or sour cherries)
½ cup water	1 Tbs. brandy or Cherry
Enough Sucaryl to sweeten	Heering
(amount depends on	⅛ tsp. almond extract
whether you are using	

☞ Wash and remove stems from cherries. Put them into a pan containing the water and Sucaryl, brought to a boil. Cover and cook over low heat for 5 minutes or until cherries are tender. Remove from heat, add the brandy and chill.

OYSTERS EN BROCHETTE

Serves 4.   Calories per serving: 175.

6 slices lean bacon	Salt and pepper
2 dozen oysters, shucked	Watercress sprigs
24 cherry tomatoes	Paprika
12 pimento-stuffed olives	

☞ Cut the bacon into 2-inch pieces. Be sure you have removed all the little pieces of shell from oysters. On 12 skewers, arrange oysters, bacon, and tomatoes with a stuffed olive in the center of each skewer. Sprinkle lightly with salt and pepper. Place prepared skewers on baking dish. Preheat broiler and place dish 3 inches below flame. Broil about 3 minutes, until bacon is crisp. Serve on warm plates, garnished with watercress and sprinkled with paprika.

TOTAL CALORIES FOR THE DAY: 611, INCLUDING
58 OF SNACKS

37	*Breakfast*	190	*Lunch*	326	*Dinner*
35	1 slice gluten toast	105	Fish chowder*	164	Stuffed beef-burger*
2	Wild strawberry jam (diet)	50	Grapefruit sections and watercress	25	Celery and beets*
	Black coffee	35	1 fresh peach	62	Beet greens with butter
	Midmorning drink		Tea with lemon	30	Cucumber, tomato, green pepper, and red onions with vinegar, pepper, and salt
			Midafternoon broth	45	Fresh green applesauce*
					Black coffee
				58	6 oz. skim milk at bedtime

FISH CHOWDER

Two 8-oz. servings. Calories per serving: 105.

1 tsp. butter	Pinch of thyme
¼ cup onion, finely diced	1 bouillon cube
½ lb. codfish	¾ cup skim milk
1 tsp. parsley, minced	

[*continued*]

☞ Melt butter in saucepan. Add onion and let cook for 1 minute. Cut fish in 1-inch cubes and add to onion. Add ¾ cup water, parsley, thyme, and bouillon cube. Let simmer over low heat until fish is tender. Add the milk and season to taste with salt and pepper. Heat thoroughly but do not boil.

STUFFED BEEFBURGER

Serves 4.   Calories per serving: 164.

1 Tbs. butter	1 Tbs. fine breadcrumbs
½ cup mushrooms, finely chopped	⅛ tsp. salt
	Pepper
¼ cup celery, finely chopped	Pinch rosemary
1 Tbs. onion, finely chopped	½ lb. ground steak
¼ tsp. paprika	½ cup vegetable broth (use
1½ tsps. skim milk	bouillon cube)
1 Tbs. chopped parsley	1½ tsps. flour
1 Tbs. grated carrot	

☞ Melt butter in frying pan and sauté mushrooms, celery, and onion. Sprinkle with paprika. Cook over low heat, covered, for 10 minutes. Remove from stove and add milk, parsley, carrot, breadcrumbs, salt, pepper, and rosemary. Mix thoroughly. Divide the meat into 4 parts. Place in muffin cups, forming a cup. Divide stuffing among the 4 cups, mounding it up. Pour the bouillon in the frying pan and bring to a boil. Mix the 1½ tablespoons flour with 1 tablespoon cold water and when smooth pour it into the boiling broth. Cook for a minute or so, stirring constantly, then pour into hamburger cups. Bake uncovered in a moderate oven (350 degrees) for 30 minutes, basting twice.

CELERY AND BEETS

Serves 4. Calories per serving: 25.

1⅓ cups cooked sliced celery   Salt
⅔ cup cooked sliced beets   Fresh chopped mint

☞ Mix celery and beets. Season. Reheat 5 to 10 minutes. Add mint.

FRESH GREEN APPLESAUCE

☞ When you see those first new apples, all green and sour, take some home, make applesauce sweetened with Sucaryl, and add cinnamon. Tastes just like apple pie without the crust.

TOTAL CALORIES FOR THE DAY: 607, INCLUDING 59 OF SNACKS

28	*Breakfast*	245	*Lunch*	275	*Dinner*
28	4 oz. Mott's 5-Fruit Drink Black coffee	180	3 oz. lean corned beef	155	Sweetbreads and mush-rooms*
		50	½ oz. Swiss cheese	30	Broiled tomato
1	Midmorning drink	15	Lemonade ice* Tea with lemon	15	Mixed green salad
				75	Jellied honey-dew mold*
			Midafternoon tea		Black coffee
				58	6 oz. skim milk at bedtime

LEMONADE ICE

Serves 3.   Calories per serving: 15.

> 1 can Libby's low-calorie   1½ cups cracked ice
>   lemonade mix, frozen

☞ Place in blender and whizz until the consistency of a frozen daiquiri. And if you don't know what that is like, until it looks snowy. Eat slowly and enjoy. Don't you wish they would make all those other frozen things in a low-calorie product? Think what variety we could have.

SWEETBREADS AND MUSHROOMS

Serves 6.   Calories per serving: 155.

3 pairs sweetbreads
3 cups water
1 Tbs. vinegar
2 tsps. salt
1 Tbs. butter
2 onions, chopped

½ lb. sliced mushrooms
1 Tbs. flour
¼ tsp. black pepper
1 cup cooked peas
2 Tbs. parsley, chopped

☞ Wash the sweetbreads and soak in cold water 20 minutes. Drain and combine with 3 cups water, vinegar, and 1 teaspoon salt. Bring to a boil and cover. Simmer for 20 minutes. Let cool in the stock 20 minutes. Drain, reserving 1 cup of the stock. Remove the membranes and dice the sweetbreads. Melt the butter in a skillet. Sauté the onions 5 minutes. Add the mushrooms and cook for 5 minutes more. Sprinkle with the flour, then blend in the stock, stirring constantly, until it boils. Add the pepper, peas, and chopped parsley and the remaining salt. Cover and cook over low heat for 10 minutes.

JELLIED HONEYDEW MOLD

Serves 8.   Calories per serving: 75.

2 envelopes D-Zerta strawberry gelatin
2 envelopes D-Zerta lemon
   gelatin
2 cups boiling water

2 cups cold water
½ medium honeydew melon
½ cup sliced strawberries
½ cup lemon sherbet for
   garnish

☞ Dissolve the strawberry and lemon gelatins in hot water in a large bowl. Stir in the cold water. Pour ½ cup into a lightly oiled 6-cup bowl. Place bowl in a pan of ice and water to speed up the setting time. Chill until softly set. Keep the rest of the gelatin mixture at room temperature. Scoop seeds from honeydew melon. Slice half into 8 thin wedges, pare each, then trim off inside of each slice, leaving a band about ¼ inch thick. Dice trimmings and save. Place the melon slices spoke-fashion in the softly set gelatin so that the slices meet in the center. Chill.

Carefully spoon in another ½ cup gelatin and chill this until sticky-firm. Trim the top edges of the melon slices even with the top of the mold, so that when it is turned out, it will sit flat. While the mold is chilling, chill the remaining gelatin until it is the consistency of unbeaten egg white. Fold in the diced honeydew and strawberries. Carefully spoon into the chilled mold. Chill in refrigerator overnight. Cut balls from the remaining half melon with a melon-ball cutter. When ready to serve, remove from mold and garnish with melon balls and the lemon sherbet.

TOTAL CALORIES FOR THE DAY: 609½,
INCLUDING 59 OF SNACKS

25	*Breakfast*	92½	*Lunch*	433	*Dinner*
25	½ cup tomato juice	12½	Borscht (page 12)	409	Baked spareribs with sauerkraut*
	Black coffee	50	Greek salad*		
1	Midmorning drink	30	Seedless grapes Tea with lemon	15	Mixed green salad
				9	Lime D-Zerta Black coffee
				58	6 oz. skim milk at bedtime

GREEK SALAD

Serves 6.   Calories per serving: 50.

2 filets of salt herring	6 radishes, sliced thin
1 onion, sliced thin	¼ cup cider vinegar
1 green pepper, diced	¼ tsp. freshly ground black
1 cup shredded cabbage	pepper
2 tomatoes, skinned and cubed	¼ tsp. liquid Sucaryl

☞ Soak the herring in cold water for 1 hour. Drain. Cut in 1-inch slices. Combine in a glass bowl the rest of the vegetables and the herring. Mix the vinegar, pepper, and Sucaryl together and pour over the herring mixture. Toss lightly and chill for 1 hour.

[*continued*]

BAKED SPARERIBS
WITH SAUERKRAUT

Serves 4. Calories per serving: 409. ■ *If you parboil the spareribs for about 3 or 4 minutes, a lot of the fat is removed and the cooking process is started.*

<table>
<tr><td>1½ qts. sauerkraut</td><td>Salt and pepper</td></tr>
<tr><td>4 lbs. parboiled spareribs</td><td>1 onion, sliced thin</td></tr>
<tr><td>(6 ribs per person is
allowed)</td><td>4 peeled medium potatoes</td></tr>
</table>

☞ Preheat the oven to 400 degrees. Place the sauerkraut in a mound in the center of a small roasting pan. Season the parboiled spareribs with salt and pepper. Fold the ribs in half and place the thinly sliced onion between the folds. Cover the sauerkraut with the folded spareribs. Baste frequently with the sauerkraut juice. Bake uncovered in a hot oven until nicely browned. Turn the ribs and brown the other side. Add water if necessary. Cover the pan as soon as the ribs are brown. Reduce the temperature to 350 degrees. Parboil the potatoes. When the meat is nearly done, about 1½ hours, uncover it and place the whole potatoes around it, turning them often so they may brown on all sides.

TOTAL CALORIES FOR THE DAY: 648, INCLUDING 58 OF SNACKS

47	*Breakfast*	140	*Lunch*	403	*Dinner*
12	4 oz. diet cranberry juice	10	Clear chicken broth	364	Lamb chop creole*
35	1 slice gluten toast	25	Asparagus vinaigrette	15	Fresh spinach
	Black coffee	75	Stuffed egg	15	Mixed green salad
	Midmorning drink	30	1 small bunch seedless grapes	9	Cherry D-Zerta
			Tea with lemon		Black coffee
			Midafternoon drink	58	6 oz. skim milk at bedtime

LAMB CHOP CREOLE

Serves 4.   Calories per serving: 364.

4	lamb chops, ¼ lb. each	¼ cup onion, chopped
1½	cups tomato juice	Salt and pepper to taste
¼	cup green pepper, chopped	

☞ Brown the chops all lovely and golden in your Teflon pan. Add the rest of the ingredients. Simmer covered for 30 minutes, until tender.

TOTAL CALORIES FOR THE DAY: 633, INCLUDING
58 OF SNACKS

12	*Breakfast*	250	*Lunch*	313	*Dinner*
12	½ cup diet cranberry juice Black coffee	80	1 cup Campbell's vegetable soup	120	Cod à la Portuguaise*
	Midmorning low-calorie drink	20	½ cup diet coleslaw	42	½ cup fresh peas
		100	1 fresh pear with	20	½ cup mashed turnip
		50	½ oz. Camembert cheese Tea with lemon Midafternoon tea	131	Banana delight* Black coffee
				58	6 oz. skim milk at bedtime

COD À LA PORTUGUAISE

Serves 4. Calories per serving: 120.

1 lb. cod filets
Pepper
1 onion, finely chopped
1 clove garlic, crushed
¼ cup parsley, coarsely
   chopped

Sprig of thyme
3 tomatoes, peeled, seeded,
   cored and coarsely
   chopped
½ cup dry white wine

☞ Season the filets with pepper. Place them in a heavy saucepan with the rest of the ingredients and bring to a boil. Reduce the heat and simmer gently, covered, for about 10 minutes. Carefully remove the fish so that it retains its shape.

Place on a heated serving plate and keep warm. Reduce the liquid by half. Pour the sauce over the fish and serve at once.

BANANA DELIGHT

Serves 6.   Calories per serving: 131.

4 eggs	3 bananas
1 tsp. lemon juice	2 Tbs. toasted almonds,
1 tsp. Sucaryl	chopped
2 cups whipped topping	

☞ Whip the eggs and lemon juice until thick and light. Cook and stir over hot (not boiling) water about 5 minutes. Stir in the Sucaryl. Remove from heat. Fold in 1 cup of the whipped topping. Slice bananas into 6 dessert glasses. Cover with the sauce. Garnish with the other cup of topping. Scatter the almonds on top. Chill. Who's dieting?

TOTAL CALORIES FOR THE DAY: 610, INCLUDING
58 OF SNACKS

28	*Breakfast*	137	*Lunch*	387	*Dinner*
28	½ cup Mott's	15	Cold consommé	260	Beef stew
	5-Fruit Drink	70	Carrot and		Gaston*
	Black coffee		celery salad*	65	Spring salad*
		52	½ cup fresh	62	Grape ice
	Midmorning		pineapple		supreme*
	drink		Tea with lemon		Black coffee
			Midafternoon	58	6 oz. skim milk
			tea		at bedtime

CARROT AND CELERY SALAD

Serves 6.   Calories per serving: 70.

5 stalks celery, diced fine
1 small can of peas, drained
5 carrots, scraped and grated
1 small jar low-calorie sweet-

pickle relish, well drained
2 Tbs. low-calorie mayonnaise
2 Tbs. low-calorie sour cream

☞ Combine the first 4 ingredients. Moisten with the mayonnaise mixed with the sour cream and spoon into crisp lettuce cups.

BEEF STEW GASTON (whoever he is)

Serves 6.   Calories per 1-cup serving: 260. ▪ *Taste better the second day, so do it ahead.*

2 lbs. beef
1½ cloves garlic, pressed
1 large onion, chopped
1 cup bouillon
1 cup canned tomato sauce
12 peppercorns
3 whole cloves

¼ cup parsley, chopped
½ bay leaf
½ cup dry white wine
6 small potatoes
6 carrots
1 stalk celery, chopped

☞ Brown the meat in the Teflon pan. Combine and heat to boiling in the same pan the next 8 ingredients. Put the meat back in and simmer, closely covered, for 2 or 3 hours, until the meat is very tender. During the last hour of cooking, put in the wine and the rest of the vegetables.

SPRING SALAD

Serves 6.   Calories per serving: 65.

3 Tbs. wine vinegar
1 Tbs. salad oil
1 tsp. salt
¼ tsp. pepper
½ tsp. dry mustard
1 cup cooked asparagus tips
1 cup cooked green beans

1 cup cooked green peas
6 radishes, sliced
2 hard-boiled eggs, chopped
2 Tbs. chives, chopped
1 Tbs. parsley, chopped
¼ cup diet mayonnaise

☞ In a salad bowl mix the vinegar, oil, salt, pepper, and mustard. Add the rest of the ingredients except the mayonnaise. Toss lightly and let marinate for 20 minutes. Blend in the mayonnaise and serve.

[continued]

GRAPE ICE SUPREME

Serves 4.   Calories per serving: 62.

1 cup unsweetened grape
    juice
½ cup crushed diet-pack
    pineapple

1 cup water
2 Tbs. cream sherry
1 Tbs. Sucaryl

☞ Combine all ingredients. Mix well. Freeze to a mush in ice tray. Remove from tray. Beat, return to tray, freeze firm. Serve.

TOTAL CALORIES FOR THE DAY: 604, INCLUDING 58 OF SNACKS

65	*Breakfast*	147	*Lunch*	334	*Dinner*
28	½ cup Mott's Grape-Apple drink	100	Egg Florentine (page 58)*	190	Bouillabaisse (page 154)
35	1 slice gluten toast	47	Blueberry compote*	54	1 slice French bread
2	Diet wild strawberry jam		Tea with lemon	15	Mixed green salad
	Black coffee		Midafternoon tea	75	Fresh fruit bowl
	Midmorning drink				Black coffee
				58	6 oz. skim milk at bedtime

BLUEBERRY COMPOTE

Calories per 4-ounce serving: 47.

1 pint blueberries   1 cup water
1 Tbs. Sucaryl

☞ Bring blueberries, Sucaryl, and water to a boil. Chill.

TOTAL CALORIES FOR THE DAY: 604, INCLUDING
58 OF SNACKS

70 *Breakfast*	150 *Lunch*	326 *Dinner*
70 1 soft-boiled egg	100 Lobster salad*	201 Dolmas (stuffed
Black coffee	50 Lemon sherbet	grape
Midmorning	(page 84)	leaves)*
drink	Tea with lemon	60 Salad à la
	Midafternoon	Grècque*
	tea	65 Vanilla yogurt
		Black coffee
		58 6 oz. skim milk
		at bedtime

LOBSTER SALAD

Serve 1.   Calories per serving: 100.

¾ cup cooked lobster meat   ½ cup celery, diced
1 Tbs. low-calorie   Lettuce leaf
   mayonnaise

☞ Mix the first 3 ingredients and place in lettuce leaf. Can
be dusted with paprika, if desired.

DOLMAS (STUFFED GRAPE LEAVES)

Serves 8.   Calories per serving (4 each): 201.

30 young, fresh grape leaves   ¼ cup salad oil
 2 cups onions, finely chopped   2 Tbs. dill, finely chopped
½ cup rice   2 Tbs. parsley, finely chopped

¼ cup pine nuts
¼ cup dried currants
1 cup lamb, finely minced

1 Tbs. butter
2 cups boiling stock

☞ *To prepare fresh grape leaves:* Drop young, pale green grape leaves into boiling water and blanch till the color darkens. Remove leaves, drain them on a skimmer. Place shiny side down on a board. Roll the filling in ¾-inch balls. If there is rice in the filling, do not put more than 2 teaspoons of filling on each leaf, as the rice swells. Set one ball near the broad end of the leaf, fold over the right and left segments, then roll the leaf from the bottom as if you were rolling a cigarette. Place loose-end-down for cooking. It's very easy. Mix all the ingredients for the filling and do as directed above. Put the rolls in a single layer in a large casserole. Place a plate on top to give weight during the cooking. Simmer over low heat or in the oven for 1½ hours. These can be served hot or cold. In summer, very cold.

SALAD À LA GRÈCQUE

Serves 6.   Calories per serving: 60.

2 Tbs. olive oil
2 Tbs. wine vinegar
1 tsp. salt
½ tsp. freshly ground black
   pepper
1 clove garlic
1 bay leaf

¼ tsp. thyme
2 cups chicken broth
2 small zucchini, sliced thin
12 small white onions
1 small eggplant, peeled and
   julienned
½ cup green beans

☞ Combine everything in a saucepan and cook over low heat for 10 minutes. Remove the vegetables, strain the liquid, and cook over high heat until reduced to half the original quantity. Pour over the vegetables and serve very cold.

TOTAL CALORIES FOR THE DAY: 655, INCLUDING
59 OF SNACKS

135	*Breakfast*	171	*Lunch*	290	*Dinner*
30	2 oz. low-calorie cranberry juice with 2 oz. orange juice	136	Vegetable plate	245	Chicken Louisiane
		25	¼ cup peas	15	Mixed green salad
		50	¼ cup corn	30	2 fresh plums
70	Poached egg on	27	½ cup broccoli heads		Black coffee
35	1 slice gluten toast	34	½ cup beets	58	6 oz. skim milk at bedtime
1	Midmorning low-calorie drink	35	Fruit D-Zerta Tea with lemon		
			Midafternoon tea		

VEGETABLE PLATE

Serves 1. Calories per serving: 136.

☞ This can be either hot or cold. If you serve it cold put a little low-calorie salad dressing on the vegetables an hour or so ahead of time. It takes time to sink in, you know.

CHICKEN LOUISIANE

Serves 6. Calories per serving: 245.

1 3 lb. chicken, cut up
1 Tbs. olive oil
4 cups canned tomatoes
   Speck of cayenne pepper
¼ tsp. freshly ground black
      pepper
1 bay leaf

¼ tsp. thyme
1 Tbs. parsley, finely minced
3 cloves garlic
¼ tsp. basil
½ cup onion, finely chopped
½ cup red wine

☞ Wipe off the chicken. Brown the pieces in the Teflon pan. In another pan simmer the tomatoes until they are slightly reduced in liquid. Add pepper, cayenne, thyme, parsley, bay leaf, garlic, and basil. Cook until the tomatoes are thick. Remove the chicken from the Teflon pan, add the olive oil, and cook the onions and green peppers until they are wilted. Add the wine, combine everything, and simmer covered 45 minutes.

TOTAL CALORIES FOR THE DAY: 626, INCLUDING
58 OF SNACKS

78 **Breakfast**	99 **Lunch**	391 **Dinner**
50 ½ cup Puffed Rice	80 Deviled egg (page 31) on	206 Leg of lamb,* eastern Mediter- ranean style
22 2 oz. skim milk	10 Watercress, garnished with scallions, radishes, cucumber, and green pepper	55 Summer squash medley*
6 Sprinkle of blueberries		15 Mixed green salad
Black coffee		115 Cantaloupe Lillian Russell*
Midmorning drink	9 Lemon D-Zerta Tea with lemon	Black coffee
	Midafternoon tea	58 6 oz. skim milk at bedtime

LEG OF LAMB

Calories in three slim slices: 206.

5 lb. leg of lamb, trimmed	1 bunch scallions, chopped
Salt and freshly ground black pepper	8 stalks fresh mint, chopped
	1 cup stock or bouillon

☞ Preheat oven to 450 degrees. Rub the meat with salt and pepper. Place the roast on a rack in a baking pan and cook until browned, 15 or 20 minutes. Reduce the temperature to 325 degrees and continue roasting until the meat is rare (140 degrees F. on a meat thermometer). Cover the meat with the scallions and mint. Add the stock to the pan and return the meat to the oven. Roast until done (175 degrees on the meat thermometer). Baste frequently with the liquid in the pan. Before serving, run a few ice cubes through the pan gravy to remove some of the fat and serve with the delightful mint sauce that results from this easy way of cooking a leg of lamb.

SUMMER SQUASH MEDLEY

Serves 6.   Calories per serving: 55.

2 medium yellow squash	½ tsp. Sucaryl
2 Tbs. cooking oil	¼ tsp. oregano
1 onion, chopped fine	½ tsp. salt
1 1-lb. can tomatoes, drained and cut up	⅛ tsp. pepper

☞ Scrub the squash. Slice thin and boil in lightly salted water until tender, 10 or 15 minutes. Drain well. Heat the oil in the Teflon pan and sauté the onion for 10 minutes. Add the squash and all the remaining ingredients. Mix well, but tenderly; cover and cook for 10 more minutes.

CANTALOUPE LILLIAN RUSSELL

Serves 4.   Calories per serving: 115.   ■   *This one goes back to my childhood. Daddy always roared out when he saw it being carried into the dining room, "Ah, Lillian Russell! There was a woman!" Sometimes I wish her style would come back. I wouldn't be sitting here writing this book.*

1 medium cantaloupe, peeled, seeded, and chilled	2 egg whites Generous pinch cream of tartar
4 small scoops vanilla ice milk	2 Tbs. dry skim milk powder
2 tsp. brandy	½ tsp. Sucaryl

[continued]

☞ Cut the cantaloupe in 4 slices. Place on cookie tin on aluminum foil. Place scoop of hard ice milk in each center. Poke a hole in each scoop and pour in ½ teaspoon brandy. Beat the egg whites and cream of tartar until stiff moist peaks form. Add the milk solids and Sucaryl and cover each cantaloupe slice completely. Bake in a preheated 500-degree oven for 5 minutes, or until meringue is lightly browned.

TOTAL CALORIES FOR THE DAY: 609, INCLUDING
59 OF SNACKS

60 *Breakfast*	98 *Lunch*	392 *Dinner*
25 ½ cup tomato juice	55 1 cup Campbell's chicken soup with rice	300 Flamenco veal chops*
35 1 slice gluten toast	43 ½ cup dietetic peaches	30 Stewed tomatoes
Black coffee	Tea with lemon	12 Green beans
1 Midmorning low-calorie drink	Midafternoon tea	15 Mixed green salad
		35 Spiced fruit (page 26)
		Black coffee
		58 6 oz. skim milk at bedtime

FLAMENCO VEAL CHOPS

Serves 6. Calories per serving: 300.

6 loin veal chops	½ cup pitted black olives
Seasoned flour	½ cup green pepper, chopped
¼ cup olive oil	½ cup onion, chopped
1 10-oz. can beef consommé	¼ cup pimento, chopped
2 tsps. grated lemon rind	2 Tbs. capers
1 Tbs. Worcestershire sauce	

☞ Flour the chops, then knock most of it off. Brown in the Teflon pan in the olive oil. Add the consommé and the rest of the ingredients. Cover pan. Cook over low heat for 40 to 45 minutes. Turn chops occasionally until tender.

The Last Word

Here we are at the end of the book, and I hope the end of your diet is in sight. Watch your weight now, and if you gain even a pound, choose your favorite diet-day menu and repeat it. If your weight does not go down, diet for a second day. We watch ourselves all year very carefully during the week—from Monday to Friday, that is—so that when we are being social on Saturday and Sunday we can be carefree. Continue cooking with low fat in your Teflon pan. I hope that many of the tricks I have taught you will have become so firmly embedded in your kitchen behavior that you will keep on using them automatically. It won't do you any harm. The older we grow the less we need large amounts of food. It is very easy to slump and allow the extra weight to creep back. It is also just as easy to check your weight every morning, and do something about it immediately. That very day. This is the secret of dieting success.

I'm glad that you feel better, that you have those pretty new clothes, that the doctor is proud of you, and that your back doesn't ache or your ankles get all puffy.

I'll bet I'm not half as glad as you are.

TWENTY

Tricks, Tips, and Suggestions for Successful Dieting

ONE: Make up your mind.

TWO: Throw out all those leftovers.

THREE: When you go shopping, look at each item and ask yourself: "Is this thing going to look well on my hips?" If you say *no*, put it back on the shelf. Shop immediately after eating. Never go to the supermarket at 11:30 A.M. or you will buy everything in the store.

FOUR: Don't eat because you're bored.

FIVE: Don't eat to be sociable.

SIX: Find a fat friend and set up a contest.

SEVEN: Weigh and measure your food portions until you can do it by eye.

EIGHT: Omit salt.

NINE: Admit you are dieting, particularly to yourself.

TEN: No second helpings, except for nondieting family or friends.

ELEVEN: Walk more.

TWELVE: Keep low-calorie snacks in the refrigerator and raid it if you get desperate.

THIRTEEN: Don't be afraid of something new and different, provided it is low in calories.

FOURTEEN: Learn about spices and condiments. Most of them add nothing but flavor—no calories.

FIFTEEN: Buy a new dress a size too small. Diet yourself into it.

SIXTEEN: Scotch-tape a picture of yourself at your fattest on the refrigerator door. This *ought* to stop you.

SEVENTEEN: If you drink, quit.

EIGHTEEN: Use low-calorie soft drinks.

NINETEEN: Stop eating bread.

TWENTY: Eat more salads.

INDEX